Simone's Maxims

Updated and Expanded:

Understanding Today's Academic Medical Centers

Joseph V. Simone, MD

Editorial Rx Press
Orange Park, FL

Published by Editorial Rx Press
Editorial Rx Press, Registered Office:
P.O. Box 794, Orange Park, FL 32067
www.editorialrxpress.com

First Editorial Rx Press Printing April 2012

10 9 8 7 6 5 4 3 2 1

ISBN 978-0-9832958-9-1

Reprinted by permission from the American Association
for Cancer Research: Simone JV: Understanding
Academic Medical Centers: Simone's Maxims.
Clin Cancer Res. 1999;5: 2281-2285.

Printed in the United States of America

Original cover and book design by biographics
www.biographicsweb.com

CONTENTS

PREFACE

The first version of this work was published as an editorial in *Clinical Cancer Research* in 1999. Two other versions with minor revisions were written for my own use but were never published in a journal or a book. This is an edited and expanded version of the original publication with the addition of several more maxims. Also, this book contains a greatly expanded treatment of the topics covered in the maxims; the maxims are now paired with a collection of topically relevant essays that I have written over the years for *Oncology Times*. These essays have also been updated and edited where necessary.

INTRODUCTION

Academic medical centers today represent a unique fusion of traditional academia, hospital functions, several levels of education, and, above all, patients. They are complex organizations trying to discharge a conflicting melange of responsibilities. This turmoil can be perplexing to individuals working in such an environment, especially trainees and younger and mid-level faculty. They are the most vulnerable in the system and may not yet have sufficient experience to use as a reliable touchstone. Are there lessons or guidelines that can be learned and used as one proceeds through a career? Can one better understand academic institutions, their leaders and processes? Are there some consistencies that broadly apply to help negotiate the increasingly stormy seas?

Like many colleagues, the more my career has involved administrative and leadership responsibilities, the more I have become a student of academic medical centers and how they function. During my career I have moved through the trainee and faculty ranks and been the responsible leader at the section and department levels. I have also had senior administrative responsibilities at major academic medical centers: St. Jude Children's Research Hospital and the University of Tennessee; Stanford University Medical Center; Memorial Sloan-Kettering Cancer Center; the University of Utah; and the University of Florida. Throughout those positions I have gained some wisdom and many battle scars. To make some sense of my experiences and what I learned from others, I began years ago to establish personal rules of thumb, "maxims," to discern some meaningful patterns in the seemingly chaotic events and baffling human behavior. Thus, *Simone's Maxims* emerged to guide my own judgment.

These maxims concern the behavior of academic medical institutions, their leaders, and their faculty from the individual's point of view. They were accumulated and developed from years of personal experience and many mistakes, as well as occasional revelations, both personal and borrowed from others. Although these maxims are personal, each is supported by the experience of some colleagues. I am confident that my experience is not unique, and that at least some will resonate with others in academic medicine, each of whom will have personal variations. The maxims are offered mainly to those below the full professor level because they are less experienced and also because we full professors tend to believe we know it all. They have grown and evolved over time and they are likely to continue to do so; these are no tablets from Moses, to be sure. The maxims, paired with the commentaries from my columns in *Oncology Times*, are contained in five categories: institutions, leadership, recruiting, job changes, and values and success.

MAXIMS ON INSTITUTIONS

> **Institutions don't love you back.**

This first maxim may sound cynical, but the relationship between a trainee, faculty member or any employee and the institution is impersonal and contractual, whether written or not. Institutional leaders must make decisions that are not personal, but usually have positive or negative personal consequences. One cannot expect the same consideration as one may receive in a family. Despite overwhelming evidence to the contrary, it is surprising how often even full professors believe they deserve special consideration because of loyalty, longevity or past productivity. A wise colleague once told me that job security was the ability to move to another job (because of professional independence). One must keep in mind that institutional relationships are really with persons, who can and sometimes do love you back. My fondest memories of places I've been are of co-workers and patients, not "the institution." If they moved on, my attachment moved with them. For any one of us, good co-workers and solid leaders make what we value in the institution. Recognizing them, the values they represent and what they do for us are far more important than loyalty to an impersonal institution.

> **Institutions have infinite time horizons to attain goals, but an individual has a relatively short productive period.**

There is little incentive for an institution to rapidly cut through the bureaucratic morass. A faculty member may waste a key part of his career tilting at windmills or agitating politically out of frustration. An institution looks out at its large pool of ever-changing stars of the moment, so it can (and often must) look at the cumulative progress of all, a measure not possible for an individual. Therefore, when the institution's realistic time frame for change is so long as to seriously threaten one's productivity or momentum, a change of job or focus must be contemplated.

> **Institutional reputations (and those of its departments and divisions) change long after the time of their successes and failures; individual reputations change more quickly.**

Those responsible for changes are often long gone before their impact, for good or ill, is fully felt. The individual is forced to gauge the trajectory and often glacial speed of institutional change, no matter how difficult this can be, in order to judge whether the light at the end of the tunnel is daylight or an oncoming train. In other words, it is best not to confuse the current reputation of your division or laboratory with your own. You can wither in a well-known lab and you can grow in a not-so-famous environment.

> **Members of most institutional committees consist of about 30% who will work at it despite other pressures and 20% who are idiots, status seekers or troublemakers.**

The remainder consists of those who don't show up, attend because they have nothing better to do, or who can't or won't spend much energy on it. (Not incidentally, this same percentage applies to boards of directors, who, I hasten to add, are the owners of non-profit institutions such as academic medical centers. The higher up you go in such institutions, the more important it is to know into which category each trustee fits, because trustees have enormous influence and they turn over rarely.) The most successful committees have hard-working chairmen who prepare themselves and the members before meetings, call meetings only when essential and engage members in a productive manner. No academic committee meeting should exceed 60 minutes, preferably 50. No one ever complains of meetings being too short. Longer meetings are usually due to poor leadership, poor organization or a lack of purpose.

> **Institutional incompetents and trouble-makers are often transferred to another area where they continue to be incompetent or troublemakers.**

They force others to pick up the slack or repair their mistakes, reducing everyone's efficiency. If this continues for long, those who are consistently unproductive may become the majority because the competent learn that the institution sees no virtue in hard work and collaboration. As difficult as it may be, the best solution for all parties is to fire the individual. This is true despite the fact that one must deal with past evaluations that have been unrealistically positive, complicated grievance procedures, bureaucratic barriers, and the unpleasantness of confrontation. I have been burned several times on this issue so I have a couple of safeguards. I'll discuss faculty later, but for non-faculty, at the hiring interview I usually tell them that it might not work out-- because of them, because of me, or just because of bad chemistry. Therefore, if I must terminate them, it is a bit easier for both of us. It is also easier to terminate an employee during the probationary period.

> **In institutions as well as in personal life, there is such a thing as too much money.**

The risk is the same for both. The most serious risk, almost unavoidable because the money is readily available, is that money is spent on projects that have not been screened critically, are only marginally related to the core mission of the institution, simply because it is there and might be lost if it isn't used, or to please a rich donor (the donor wants a monument to himself) when there is no pressing need for that project. The worst outcome is that the institution becomes profligate and adapts to the new loose and wasteful standard, so when financial hard times return, as they always do, they are in a pickle because they have become addicted to the easy access to resources. At best, the institution sees this coming and makes quick adjustments. At worst, the situation leads to layoffs, executive exits, a crippled mission and a blackened reputation of the institution and a crippled ability to recruit top talent.

> **Institutions have an almost immutable culture that drives important decisions.**

The light bulb of this lesson went on later in my career as I began to move around. Yes, change can be made around the edges and in smaller units, but for a medical school or university, a culture has developed over many years and through many administrations. Substantive changes that do occur are usually incited from the outside, not from within.

> **An institution will always outlast a dissenting individual, regardless of the merit of the case.**

Such an employee or faculty member may waste a valuable part of his or her career tilting at windmills or agitating politically out of frustration. With the limited energy and time one has for career development or programmatic fulfillment, it is often best for one in an unproductive situation to cut one's losses, make the best possible deal for an exit and move on.

COMMENTARIES ON INSTITUTIONS

Fresh Eyes on the University Medical Center

I have trained and worked in academic medical centers from the time I entered medical school, a span of 60+ years. After completing my training I have been employed mostly by free standing cancer centers, but 10 of those years were in universities. I began a new tenure at a university a few weeks ago and this is giving me the opportunity not only to do my job, but also to observe the function and structure of university medical centers from the inside with fresh eyes and extensive experience. I will offer some observations from my prior and current experience in this column.

Why am I doing this? Although I am a fan of free-standing cancer centers, which is reflected in my experience, university-based health science centers are essential forces in determining the quality and stature of biological research in our country and they have a strong influence on the standards of medical care, particularly in their own geographic regions. They have been under severe financial, regulatory, and other pressures, worse in the past decade, from many corners of society. In this respect and many others, all university medical centers are having the same experience. Much of what I have observed over the years will resonate with those in most university medical centers. I will begin with a focus on two intramural issues.

The Hospital-Medical School Divide

The width of this chasm differs from place to place, ranging from a reasonable leap to a Grand Canyon. There are several reasons for this chasm. First, the trustees judge the performance of the chief hospital administrator mainly on the financial bottom line of hospital operations; the dean of medicine and vice president for health affairs are judged mainly on the academic success of the faculty, such as number of grants, high profile publications, and national recognition, although more and more on financial issues such as clinical income of the faculty. When the vision and incentives of these two officers are not aligned, this can lead to serial battles over the distribution of revenues.

This situation is more acute if the hospital is not under the control of the university. This can occur when the university hospital is established as a legally independent not-for-profit organization with its own board of trustees or if the hospital is owned by a for-profit organization. In the latter case, financial woes at other, non-university branches of a for-profit hospital system affect the relationship with the university over finances and programmatic development. In all of these legal relationships, because the hospital controls most of the medical revenue, the hospital's agenda can trump the university's academic agenda, in effect allowing the hospital to run the medical school.

These issues grew as a result of the explosive growth of the amount of money to be made in health care services. The enactment of Medicare in 1965 began the progressive change in the financial landscape of medicine, which was accelerated by the almost universal availability of health insurance through one's employer. New technology fueled these costs even higher. Clinical revenues became major sources of income for clinical departments in medical schools. Keep in mind that research grants pay only for the research, and not all costs for the funded project at that. Clinical revenues are more plastic and at times add up to multiples of the revenue from grants, and clinical revenues can be used for needs other than salaries.

But this has been a financial two-edged sword for medical schools. Some specialist cannot bring in enough revenue to pay their salaries, especially those with no technical fees to increase the income—pediatrics, psychiatry, and some medical specialties come to mind. So the rich have to pay for the poor, which is often unpopular. Furthermore, the medical school often looks to the hospital, which gets most of the technical fees generated by the faculty, for financial help. The hospital is often unwilling to "invest" in faculty with no chance of getting a "return on (financial) investment," thus there are discordant visions.

At some university medical centers, the vice president for health affairs is the CEO of both the hospital and the medical school, with the hospital administrator and the dean of the school of medicine reporting to him/her. This provides a better opportunity for aligning the vision and incentives of both entities. Success then often depends on the management skills and personality of the vice president. Some of the same tensions can arise, but a single person can adjudicate them more readily with authority over both.

The Silo Factor

The departmental structure in university medical centers often is antithetical to the modern multidisciplinary care model. Each chairman has his/her own agenda that is seldom in sync with other chairmen, and he/she controls resources and the power of faculty appointments and promotions that have a major impact on the ability to develop any coordinated program, such as oncology, which is rarely a department. Oncology patients may make up a minority of a general surgeon's practice; this situation often does not encourage participation in clinical research, multidisciplinary clinics, and tumor boards. The lack of focus makes it difficult to develop programs that offer anything extraordinary that goes beyond community hospital care.

Another issue in this setting is that a chairman, of medicine for example, may espouse a faculty model that cannot be sustained in a busy oncology service. If all medical oncologists are expected to sustain a competitive, grant-funded laboratory, it may be impossible for them to carry a full load of cancer patient care. A part-time medical oncologist will not generate enough clinical revenue to cover his/her salary. Even full time academic oncologists may not do so, particularly if the hospital keeps all chemotherapy and other technical revenues. (It may be easier for other subspecialists to do lab research and clinical care well, particularly when they are responsible for patients that have less demanding needs than cancer patients.) This leads to pressure from the chairman to see more patients, which often compromises the ability to compete for research grants: a Catch 22. This can lead to frustration and flight to private practice where the agenda is more straightforward.

This "Silo Effect" of departmental isolation is difficult to overcome. The most successful cancer programs in university medical centers have sufficient control of space and independent funds to make it easier to overcome these separations by offering resources for joint appointments and startup packages, but by no means do they guarantee a convivial, collaborative relationship. In any case, it is yet another hurdle to overcome when attempting to build multidisciplinary programs.

One might say that the traditional university medical center is archaic, an attempted adaptation of the university structure first developed in medieval times. In more recent times, this may have worked with the German model of the 19th century, also adopted in other European countries, i.e. the all-inclusive department or focused institute headed by Herr Professor. The professor usually had a management role of the clinical facility and total authority over operations, appointments and such. The economics were relatively simple. The professor was paid by the state for his university work and he often had a lucrative private practice on the side. His aides were paid peanuts, if they were paid at all. (This model persists in parts of Italy.)

Today's university medical center in America that developed its present shape after World War II is an entirely different entity. It is a big business that often is suffocating under the fusion (or confusion) of competing demands using structural models with conflicting missions; it has not fully adapted to the financial and social realities of the day that profoundly influence its ability to carry out the academic mission. Thus we see the increasing strength of free-standing cancer centers and research institutes, both of which have a more unified vision of their missions. The fact that some university medical centers are doing quite well, academically and financially, is a reflection of their elite status and/or being quickly adaptable to contemporary realities. Most university medical centers have done neither, despite the best efforts of many faculty and staff, because of poor leadership, glacial responses to societal change, or an ingrained satisfaction with mediocrity.

The challenges are many and general solutions have been discussed *ad nauseum* in academic circles. But these problems are, in the end, local problems that must be solved within the institutions involved. The coordinated and consistent institutional leadership needed at all levels for bold and visionary action in university medical centers is rare indeed.

Groupthink

In the *New York Times* of 2 November 2008 ("Challenging the Crowd in Whispers, Not Shouts"), the Yale economist, Robert J. Shiller, wrote about the economic and banking collapse and why all those smart economists at the Federal Reserve and in academia failed to see it coming. He offered a plausible explanation that is also, in my view, relevant to medicine. I will summarize his article first.

Shiller points to the Congressional testimony of Alan Greenspan, former chairman of the Federal Reserve, who said he made an error in assuming markets would properly regulate themselves. He had "no idea" a disaster was in the making since the Fed's own experts and computer models simply "did not forecast" the fiscal crisis. There were warnings from the Fed staff, but no one "predicted" the outcome.

The author then recalls talking to a Miami cab driver who several years earlier had pointed to the feverish building boom as they drove past housing developments and said that surely there will be a glut followed by a crash. And there were books and articles for years before the crisis that pointed to an inevitable problem if the housing bubble continued to grow. But even during his own term on the advisory panel for the Federal Reserve Bank of New York, Shiller had expressed his own concern about a bubble "very gently," as did other members of that panel. He wondered why.

His explanation follows: "The field of social psychology provides a possible answer. In his classic book, *Groupthink*, Irving L. Janis explained how panels of experts could make colossal mistakes. People on these panels, he said, are forever worrying about their personal relevance and effectiveness, and feel that if they deviate too far from the consensus, they will not be given a serious role. They will self-censor personal doubts about the emerging group consensus if they cannot express these doubts in a formal way that conforms with apparent assumptions held by the group."

Shiller later became more forceful in his warnings and encountered an acknowledgement of the risks, but his warnings were not taken seriously. He based his predictions largely on behavioral economics, a relatively new field of study not widely accepted among economists, which proposes that speculative bubbles are caused by contagious excitement about investment prospects. Some economists recognize this in private, but few base decisions on it.

So he asks, "Why do professional economists always seem to find that concerns about bubbles are overblown or unsubstantiated?" He opines that it might be due to their training, a self-selection into the field of economics that focuses on the technical and mathematical. They are not trained in psychology; the notion that people are making huge errors in judgment is not appealing. Also, concerns about professional stature may blind them to the possibility that they are witnessing a market bubble.

Shiller's observations and conclusions may be applied to any professional group, and medicine is no exception. Even when one subtracts those who don't care or simply don't pay attention, an authoritative position may not be challenged because of the risk of alienating those in authority and being moved outside the circle of action in the organization. We see this behavior in department meetings, committees, hospitals, practice groups, and boards of trustees.

The most vivid personal recollections of such behavior occurred among members of boards of trustees of hospitals and other non-profit organizations (it may also for true of for-profits, e.g. Enron, but I have no first-hand experience). Service on these boards is voluntary and often honorific. The social dynamic usually has layers of personal agendas outside the actual duties of the trustees. Hospital boards, for example, are often populated by leaders of local community businesses who enjoy the insider information one gathers in such roles and hobnobbing with other community or social leaders. Social or business relationships among trustees can make it even harder for such a person to go against the received wisdom of the chairman or another strong, vocal member.

However, we doctors are not immune. I have seen this behavior in committees that are developing a new clinical research protocol. It is common for a specific aspect of therapy to become engrained in the beliefs of the majority so firmly that any warnings or misgivings, particularly when expressed by an investigator outside the committee, are not taken seriously. I admit to being guilty of such "groupthink" myself on occasion (I hope rarely).

It is more difficult and forgivable for a trainee to resist such behavior. And it is easier for old guys like me to speak against positions widely held by the authoritative majority; the difference in depth of experience and the risk of being ostracized are polar opposites for the trainee and old curmudgeon. It is the great majority in the middle that must be most diligent to have an open mind and avoid groupthink.

How does one do so? It helps a lot to be very well prepared before a meeting, to dig for little known information and to have data to support a position. It also helps to have one or more allies on the committee, or at least confided the misgivings to colleagues before the meeting, creating at least a sympathetic ear if not total agreement.

We are human beings and we make very bad judgments at times, often as part of a group. We have an obligation to speak up forcefully when we perceive danger and to have an open mind when others do so. Groupthink is the enemy of clearly perceiving threats and major blunders; groupthink is the enemy of creativity.

Institutional Cultures

We often hear of popular culture but less often of institutional culture. The latter is confined to a specific organization, such as a university, hospital, business, football team, oncology practice, or a state legislature. One definition of institutional culture is "common ideas and values." Often, the culture has standards that permeate the everyday lives of its members, and that are perpetuated by institutional indoctrination, actions, and leadership.

Why is institutional culture important? While it is ubiquitous and usually out of sight and mind, institutional culture has a profound impact on our work environment and our ability to succeed and prosper. If we are not careful, it can stealthily make us willing to accept lower professional or ethical standards of behavior in others and ourselves.

On the other hand, institutional culture can influence us to raise our values and our standards of professional behavior, work ethic, and productivity. If we think of our institutions' culture at all, it is usually due to a change in management, a controversial institutional decision, or the departure of a valued colleague.

The fact that an institution has a culture implies that institutions are living and potentially changeable entities, as are the people who comprise them. However, once established and accepted over a period of years, an institution's culture is very difficult to change. A few examples: a culture of poor service in a business establishment, once embedded, may require drastic means and more than one leadership generation to change because everyone, at all levels, tolerates or accepts that behavior. For the same reason, a research organization with modest expectations for productivity and the efficient use of resources will usually beget mediocre research and profligacy. People with much higher standards are either not recruited or they refuse the position because they see no similarly minded colleagues in the organization.

And closer to home, a culture of all-consuming focus on the financial bottom line in a hospital can result in only token attention to the quality of care or the workplace environment or patient access to services. This culture is sometimes perpetuated by trustees that award large annual bonuses to its executives based on the financial performance of the institution; these same trustees come to believe that a ranking among hospitals listed in *U.S. News and World Report* equals high quality care for patients, a dangerous oversimplification.

This issue becomes even more complicated and difficult to manage when two or more institutions, with invariably different cultures, try to work together. Two hospitals, two research organizations, or a hospital and a medical school come to mind. I have dealt with all three situations in my career, and others that are even more complex. The particulars may differ, but peeling away the surface invariably reveals two factors at the bottom of nearly all difficulties: money and power (or control).

The typical academic medical center consists of a college of medicine (sometimes with other health colleges) and a hospital. This, in one way or another, often leads to a clash in cultures. One would think that the missions are aligned, the goals overlap substantially, and except for the usual catfights over how to do something and how to pay for it, they would generally move forward together. And this does happen sometimes.

But at the other end of the spectrum are nasty, incessant power struggles and mistrust that cripple the missions of both. The latter situation is sometimes prevented, or at least mitigated, when a single person leads both entities, but not always.

Influences on Work Productivity and Antisocial Behavior

Anyone who has held, or aspires to hold, a management position must deal with the sometimes vexing issues of productivity and social behavior. Whether in a hospital, a practice, a laboratory, or a business enterprise, one faces a wide array of personalities and habits that people bring with them. Having had a management role for four decades, this became a keen interest of mine. Below are several interesting and relevant reports on the issue.

By coincidence, I grew up not far from the huge Hawthorne plant of Western Electric (forerunner of AT&T) at Cicero Avenue and Roosevelt Road in the Chicago area. The plant gained fame from an unlikely source. The enlightened leadership of the plant recruited George E. Mayo, a psychologist and sociologist, and others in 1924 to examine productivity, employee turnover and other work parameters. They examined the influences on productivity of pay levels, rest periods and, the one I remember best, changes in lighting.

In their studies they found that increasing the lighting of the workroom increased productivity, but so did reducing the lighting, and the increase in productivity continued even when lighting was returned to its initial level. Mayo concluded that

that the test room workers had turned into a social unit and enjoyed all the attention they were getting; they also had a sense of participation in the project. This feeling of being studied (or watched), and its positive influence on productivity, irrespective of the specific changes in the environment, became known as the Hawthorne Effect.

These studies in the mid-1920s were followed by a growing interest in the effect of the immediate environment on social behavior beyond industrial productivity, including increasingly sophisticated studies of antisocial and criminal behavior. For example, in 1982, James Q. Wilson and George L. Kelling published the "Broken Window Theory," based on the observation that an abandoned building with one broken window that is not fixed is often followed vandals breaking many other windows. If the broken window was fixed, breakage of other windows was much less likely.

In subsequent years, the behavioral effect of degraded surroundings has been followed by an increasingly scientific approach to understand how this happens. A well-designed series of Dutch studies recently published online in *Science* by Kees Keizer, Siegwart Lindenberg, and Linda Steg (www. sciencemag.org/cgi/content/abstract/1161405) addresses the influence on antisocial behavior of degradation in the immediate environment such as graffiti, littering, and illegal parking.

In one experiment the researchers hung useless paper fliers on bicycles in an alley that had a sign on the wall forbidding graffiti. There was no trashcan in the alley. The alley was watched to see how many cyclists put the flier in their pockets for later disposal and how many just threw them on the pavement or put them on another bike. On another day they created the same setup except with graffiti on the wall. With no graffiti, 19 of 77 cyclists tossed the flier away, but more than two-thirds littered when the wall had graffiti.

In another study with a €5 note left sticking out of a mailbox, 13% of passers-by pocketed the note when the mailbox was in a clean environment compared to 23% when there was trash around. The authors used visual (e.g. graffiti), auditory (loud firecrackers), legal violations (illegal parking) and other factors to demonstrate that if people see one norm being violated they are more likely to violate others, such as littering and stealing.

These and other studies have shown that disorder in the environment, including some that seem trivial by themselves, has a generalized negative effect on behavior. This finding has led to "situational prevention" by some communities to reduce crime and antisocial behavior. Authorities in Lowell, Massachusetts, found that the scrupulous and persistent cleanup of troubled neighborhoods was more effective than social services or law enforcement in this regard.

One could be influenced by these studies in several ways. One might pick up the candy wrapper that someone carelessly dropped in the corridor and put it in the trash, and maybe make it a habit. I acquired this habit not from reading studies, but from seeing my mentor do it. Or one might pick up the paper towel on the floor of the rest room (gingerly, I am sure) and drop it in the trash. (Why are men, who often consider themselves jocks, so bad at hitting the waste bin with a wad of paper towel?) We all know that when one paper towel is on the floor, others will follow, maybe by us.

Another might understand that dying potted plants in entry-way of one's workplace, unrepaired floor tiles in the elevator, and even habitual gabfests in sight of waiting patients all signal that there is some level of disorder, and that this may perpetuate additional or even habitual antisocial or professionally unacceptable behavior by ordinary people, like you and me.

And finally, one might stretch the point to make a connection to the central thesis in Malcolm Glidewell's book, *Outliers*, that "Great people aren't so great. Their own greatness is not the salient fact about them. It's the kind of fortunate mix of opportunities they've been given," e.g. Bill Gates was fortunate to go to a private school with its own computer when this was extremely rare. Glidewell gives many other examples of why, in his view, people became great. He believes that individual traits play a smaller role in explaining success while social circumstances play a larger role.

As David Brooks commented in the *New York Times* (16 December 2008), "Glidewell intelligently captures...the growing appreciation of the power of cultural patterns, social contagions, and memes...[that in the Obama Age] could lead policy makers to finally reject policies built on the assumption that people are coldly rational utility-maximizing individuals. It could cause them to focus more on policies that foster relationships, social bonds and cultures of achievement."

From the candy wrapper to the attitudes of our parents, what is around us influences whether and how we mature, how we behave, how hard we work, and how much success we have. Genetics is powerful, but so is our milieu, which one can improve much more easily for our children, our co-workers and us. My mother and father never read a scientific paper, but they knew this.

The University's (and Medical School's?) Crisis of Purpose

"The University's Crisis of Purpose" is the title of a recent essay in the *New York Times Magazine* (6 September 2009) by Dr. Drew Gilpin Faust, president of Harvard. She describes how the economic downturn has underscored the fragility of the broader purposes of the university beyond just creating a competitive workforce. "Higher education is not about results in the next quarter but about discoveries that may take – and last – decades or even centuries. Neither the abiding questions of humanistic inquiry nor the winding path of scientific research that leads ultimately to innovation and discovery can be neatly fitted within a predictable budget and timetable." In effect, she is lamenting that the core goals of higher education are becoming commodities with the focus on training rather than inquiry for its own sake. She points out that business "is now by far the most popular undergraduate major."

The essay certainly points out the problems; a solution offered by Dr. Faust is for government to provide more support, as it did with the GI Bill after World War II. But my own sensibilities resonated much more with a response to the essay published in the 20 September 2009 issue of the magazine from an emeritus professor of languages, Dr. Michael Shapiro.

Dr. Shapiro agrees that there are economic causes for the troubles in American universities, but he believes the essay "does not comprehend the three main reasons that commodification has also been allowed to pervert higher education: (1) the professionalization of university administrations, resulting in hypertrophying hordes of overpaid managers (alias chancellors, deans et al.); (2) departmental autonomy, whereby (typically small) teaching units are allowed to make personnel and curricular decisions immune to substantive scrutiny by outsiders; (3) the tenure system, which has become the last refuge of academic scoundrels and malingerers, guaranteeing them not only lifetime employment but a stranglehold on the appointment and promotion of junior faculty. If we are ever to live up to Cardinal Newman's justly celebrated vision in 'The Idea of a University,' it is these malignancies that must be rooted out first." It appears that Dr. Shapiro has very strong feelings about this issue.

My own reaction is colored by the fact that for most of my professional life I have been part of only one aspect of university life, the medical school, which certainly differs from a college of liberal arts. But when one considers the diversity of basic functions, the similarities of the problems are still greater than the differences. In fact, one may ask if there were also a crisis of purpose in medical schools and whether any of Dr. Faust's and Dr. Shapiro's concerns about universities in general also apply to medical schools.

First, some basics. Colleges and graduate programs in the liberal arts provide a broad education in the arts, language, history and the rest to provide a strong foundation for living the life of an educated person. It is hoped that the student will leave with an appreciation of the cultural span of human history with its amazing accomplishments and failures and an improved ability to think and judge wisely. This education is not immediately "practical" in the usual sense, but at its best it provides an invaluable base for any future activity.

Professional schools, such as law, nursing, pharmacy and medicine, prepare students to profess certain values and apply a body of knowledge; they are taught to represent the best interests of a patient or client and to assume responsibility for their medical or legal needs. The standards used are part of an evolving body of knowledge, which is continually shaped and modified by research, experience and social evolution. The state recognizes the importance and seriousness of these activities by requiring that aspirants possess a basic fund of knowledge and practice in a legal-ethical manner.

But professional schools are also sources of new knowledge acquired by systematic study and original research. The amount and quality of such innovative activity is balanced by training in the pragmatic professional skills. This balance varies widely among medical schools with some focused far more on research and others more on the practice of the profession. At their best, medical schools teach by example with balanced and high quality scientific innovation and medical practice. At their worst, medical schools are simply narrowly focused trade schools for physicians or scientists whose fund of knowledge will peter out in five years leaving them susceptible to every little trend proffered by pharmaceutical detail men or to following the false trails in the scientific movements of the time.

Now back to the initial issues. Dr. Faust's concern for the survival of a liberal education has no exact parallel in a professional school, but the role of education in modern basic sciences in medical schools comes close. For many students, "getting through" basic science is an unpleasant but necessary hurdle. Relatively few will become competitive scientists, but without a basic understanding of genetics, microbiology, wound healing and the rest, the student is likely to become a tradesman instead of a professional.

But the role of economics also resonates in medical schools, though in opposite directions. For Dr. Faust, it is too little money for liberal education, which cannot support itself financially. In medicine it is the 600-pound gorilla of too much money "on the table" for doctors, pharmaceutical companies, so-called non-profit hospitals, and all the other feeders at the trough. This has led to a dearth of primary care doctors, an expansion of specialists, sub-specialists and sub- sub-specialists, all of whom earn very high incomes. This in turn has led to the active recruitment of primary care doctors from areas like sub-Saharan Africa that suffer a severe shortage of doctors; this practice has been called unethical or even criminal (*Lancet* 2008; 371: 685-88). Reimbursement for primary care doctors remains low while leaders wring their hands about their decline, but do nothing. Social evolution, changes in work-hour expectations of trainees, and huge debts for medical graduates also play a role in this transformation, so economics is shaping the profession of medicine, like it or not.

Do Dr. Shapiro's concerns also apply in medical school? In my view the answer is most definitely affirmative. In many schools there is a large array of deans, associate deans, assistant deans, associate chairmen and the rest; it is mind-boggling. I don't know if they are all needed; the only sure thing is that they will spend more than half of their time sitting in committee meetings with one another.

The autonomy of chairmen in most schools is a carryover from the medieval university system in which there was a single professor of a department who was usually the smartest and best physician or scientist; he was the professor, not a professor. Remnants of that model remained in the U.S. as recently as the 1950s and persist today in some countries. But chairmen have largely become business managers whose success is measured largely in grant dollars and clinical revenue. They oversee an archaic organizational model that is increasingly being made irrelevant (or obstructionist) by multidisciplinary specialty programs in cardiology, neurology-neurosurgery and oncology, and by freestanding facilities in cardiology, oncology, orthopedics, ophthalmology and others. These more focused efforts allow a greater concentration of expertise that can provide a broader educational experience and, with a nod to the times, a greater market share.

Dr. Shapiro's third point, the tenure system, is a no-brainer for me: tenure is inappropriate in professional schools. There is brave and principled talk about the importance of productivity in medical schools but many faculty members in their 40s are given lifetime employment, irrespective of future productivity. This does not make sense. The traditional justification for tenure, freedom of speech and inquiry in controversial areas, has little relevance in professional schools. My preference is a renewable contract system with a length of 3-5 years, depending on rank.

The Flexner Report written by Abraham Flexner and funded by the Carnegie Foundation was published in 1910. It was an exhaustive study of the state of medical education in the U.S. and Canada that, in a word, was terrible. It recommended sweeping changes and higher standards for medical schools, curricula, admissions policy and oversight. The many medical trade schools were forced out of business and the quality of education improved dramatically. The result was that medicine became, in fact, a profession.

It is not too soon to think of another Flexner Report type of examination of medical schools as we approach its 100th anniversary year. Although things are not as bad as in 1910, medical schools have not adapted very well to the secular evolution of the past 60 years and the dominance of specialty training. The fraying of the social contract between physicians and the public, the endless stream of information (much of it misleading or wrong) in the public domain, and the flood of dollars into the business of medicine have perverted the profession. Computers and electronic medical records won't solve these issues; a return to first principles may.

Hubris in Medicine and Academia

I remember an event that some time ago made a lasting impression on me and ultimately triggered this column. I was sitting with top officials of a university and medical school. I was one of several people that had been invited to give advice concerning the cancer center, which had been an underachiever for many years. The cancer center also suffered from a serious lack of cohesion due in part to a common malady, departmental silos. The leaders of this highly regarded university were disappointed in the cancer center's performance and vowed to do something about it. In the course of discussions, I named some university-based cancer centers that had been very successful for many years and suggested that they visit them. The idea was to have them see and hear what steps those centers had taken to develop and sustain the functional model that not only satisfied the requirements of the National Cancer Institute, but also created a highly collaborative and academically productive environment.

The response was surprising. About one of the centers the first official said something like, "Who do they have there? I don't know of any top scientists there." I knew first-hand that this was nonsense, of course; in reality the speaker actually knew nothing about that cancer center even though it was in the same community. Another official dismissed a center I suggested because, "We have many more cancer patients than they do," which was irrelevant to the issues at hand; he conveniently disregarded the fact that his own cancer center was underperforming despite the larger patient population.

These responses reflected a classic case of hubris. These officials knew little to nothing of the workings of a modern cancer center, but because the centers I suggested were not in Ivy League institutions like the ones the officials had come from, those centers were dismissed as having nothing to teach them.

This encounter led me to recall other experiences in past years and, finally, to dig deeper into the issue of hubris in medicine and academia.

A modern definition of hubris is, "overweening pride, arrogance, snobbery or haughtiness." For the ancient Greeks hubris had a broader definition that included shaming and humiliating both a victim and the perpetrator as well, usually a person of wealth or power. In ancient Greece, and to some extent today, it also implies that a serious retribution will result from the excessive pride.

Hubris was a major issue in Greek tragedies, but also in Shakespeare's plays. In *Julius Caesar*, after denying the request of noblemen to repeal the banishment of a respected colleague, and receiving three warnings not to go to the Senate that day, the hubristic hero says on the Ides of March,

> "I am constant as the northern star,
> Of whose true-fix'd and resting quality
> There is no fellow in the firmament."

After describing himself as the unequaled star in the sky, Caesar later compares himself to an Olympian god, with fatal consequences when he goes to the Senate.

In Macbeth, the king admits to himself that he has no justification ("spur") for murdering Duncan, a relative of his, a good king, and a guest in his castle. But it is ambition and hubris that drive him and "o'erleaps" to unknown consequences. He says,

> "I have no spur
> To prick the sides of my intent, but only
> Vaulting ambition, which o'erleaps itself,
> And falls on th'other…"

One finds hubris in every walk of life; academia and medicine are no exception. The easiest target in medicine is the legendary surgeon who throws instruments when he doesn't get what he wants in the operating room. Fortunately, this is less common today. Perhaps a more serious offense by a cancer surgeon is telling the family or the patient that he "got it all," without adding or emphasizing that he only got all that he could see and that in most cases microscopic residual disease remains and can be deadly. I hasten to add that most surgeons say just that. But there are still those who are so arrogant and full of themselves that they dramatically walk from the OR in their greens and cap and mask hanging around their necks to announce triumphantly that he "got it all."

Other specialties are not immune (except, perhaps, for pediatricians...just kidding). An example is the medical oncologist who devises his own, often bizarre, therapeutic regimen that has never been tested and is based on "my experience treating other patients with good results." Of course no one else has examined his claims and he has never written the regimen down since he makes substantial modifications for each patient based on "my experience." This hubristic approach is bad medicine and may be deadly and unnecessarily expensive.

Academia is fertile ground for hubris to grow because the professorial ranks, the obsession with national rankings, and the pomp and ceremony create an atmosphere of superiority. It is a short step to believing that one's long CV, multitudes of grants, and many honors (that academics give one another) have created a superior, all-knowing being. The next step is arrogance, often evident by treating those below one's rank dismissively and impolitely. If the individual is very successful or powerful in academic terms, there is a slippery slope down to hubris.

The opposites of hubris include humility, good manners, and an open mind. The humility I speak of is not just taking care to admit one's limitations and the weakness of one's understanding or knowledge. It is much broader than that. It is trying to understand Man (our personal selves included) in all his contradictions, strengths and weaknesses. I believe Alexander

Pope in his Essay on Man made the most powerful statement in this regard. The relevant excerpt:

> "Know then thyself, presume not God to scan;
> The proper study of Mankind is Man.
> Placed on this isthmus of a middle state,
> A being darkly wise, and rudely great:
> With too much knowledge for the Sceptic side,
> With too much weakness for the Stoic's pride,
> He hangs between; in doubt to act, or rest,
> In doubt to deem himself a God, or Beast;
> In doubt his Mind or Body to prefer,
> Born but to die, and reas'ning but to err;
> Alike in ignorance, his reason such,
> Whether he thinks too little, or too much:
> Chaos of Thought and Passion, all confus'd;
> Still by himself abus'd, or disabus'd;
> Created half to rise, and half to fall;
> Great lord of all things, yet prey to all;
> Sole judge of Truth, in endless error hurl'd:
> The glory, jest and riddle of the world!"

I read "The proper study of Mankind is Man," when I was young. It strengthened my conviction to study medicine, for what else does a physician do but study Man? The study is a humbling experience, especially if within that study we are sure to include ourselves.

Lessons for Medical Centers from Apple

Apple, Inc. is one of the most admired, profitable and successful companies in the world. It has demonstrated an ability to build superior computers, to overtake and dominate existing industries in certain areas (iPod, iPhone) and to create entirely new industry segments (iPad), seemingly always a step ahead.

Gary Hamel, a management expert who writes a blog called Management 2.0 for the *Wall Street Journal,* has analyzed that success. He believes that it is rooted in "an unstinting devotion to a particular set of values." In reading his description of those values, I was struck by how many have direct parallels to today's medical centers of all types, but particularly academic medical centers. While it is true that Apple's success is based on physical products while a medical center's product is mainly services, the parallels seem to hold up. I shall briefly describe a few of Hamel's values and quotes and then draw a parallel to medical centers, particularly to clinical care.

Be passionate: "Great success is the product of a great passion—It comes from the tireless and inventive pursuit of a noble virtue...an exceptional ideal. For Apple that virtue is beauty." No doubt the beauty and apparent simplicity of form and operation—no excessive or wasted features—are keys to our admiration of Apple products.

The parallels in a medical center are obvious. Our value is healing, which encompasses cure, disease control, relief from pain and stress. We claim to be passionate about these issues, but who would we point to in our institutions whose actions may be described as consistently passionate over an extended period of time? Few, I would guess. We see many documents that list "mission, values and goals," but they often gather dust on some shelf or in a remote hallway.

Patients with serious diseases are especially vulnerable to the stress and confusion caused by issues large and small— inability to get an appointment in a reasonable time, trouble contacting the doctor or her representative, excessive delay in transmission of test results, inconvenient parking, confusion concerning prognosis or other treatment options. These and other factors are common causes of stress and are indicative of a clumsy, inefficient system. Compared to an iPhone, the "product" of medical centers is too often closer to a 1940s standard black phone with rotating dial.

Lead, don't follow: "I'm guessing that folks at Apple hate being derivative...[they sometimes borrow] but what gets them up in the morning is the chance to break new ground." We see this in some research laboratories in medical centers, but too much research is incremental. The argument is that the funding agencies won't go for radical new ideas. I don't buy that; there are countless examples of truly innovative work that has been consistently funded by peer-review panels. It helps to have a good track record, of course.

In the clinical arena, troglodytes, who are anchored in the past and hewing to "the way we have always done it," populate and dominate many medical centers. They trumpet the purchase of some new equipment or process and call it innovation when there is often no evidence that the outcomes are better, e.g. for brain tumors or prostate cancer. And some medical centers often do what Apple would never consider—attempt to be highly competitive in every area instead of focusing efforts on areas where they can excel and be a national leader. Academic medical centers are also hampered by the push and pull between different missions of education, research and medical care; a relative few excel in all three.

Aim to surprise: "Apple seems committed to exceeding expectations—to evoking "Wow" from even its most jaded customers." Hamel then quotes Jonathan Ives, head of design at Apple who was describing the new iPad: "When something exceeds your ability to understand how it works, it sort of becomes magical." To paraphrase Hamel, how many medical center executives wake up in the morning hoping to do something magical for their patients?

Be unreasonable: "Greatness doesn't come from compromises, from resigning oneself to trade-offs. It comes when trade-offs are transcended, when either/or gives way to both/and." Although Apple's products get the spotlight, Apple has a very efficient system including a "lean and agile supply chain." This back office efficiency not only saves money, but also replicates the goal for products – to be lean, efficient and beautiful. Of all the medical centers that I know, I have a hard time identifying more than a few that I would use those three words to describe.

Sweat the details: We all know of the pleasing aesthetics of Apple products, but Apple is also know for paying attention to the small details that make a positive difference in the user's experience. "And when it works instead of aggravates, it's because hundreds of people were sweating the details." A patient may have a superb physician, great nursing care and a convenient parking space, but a disrespectful check-in clerk can sour everything. Conversely, a patient may be coddled with amenities and plush upholstery, but a careless surgical procedure or medication error makes the former insignificant. It is really, really hard to have a team of caregivers who are all above average, but those details make a huge difference in patients' lives and staff pride.

Think like an engineer, feel like an artist: "A company can't produce beautiful products if the bean counters win every argument." Apple Stores are a sharp contrast to other retailers. They are neat, understatedly beautiful and efficiently organized. Also, one cannot be in the store more than a few minutes without someone offering to help. The store design and staffing are costly, but how many times have you heard someone raving about the design of any department store or electronic shop? This ambience conveys an atmosphere of competence, efficiency and expertise. The same can happen to a patient who walks into a well-designed medical center. Unfortunately, that is an uncommon event because most centers convey an overwhelming sense of unfathomable complexity and imposing scale, calling attention to one's smallness. I am a physician and that is how I feel when I enter many medical centers.

Of course Apple and medical centers differ fundamentally in many ways, but the principles that have made Apple successful can also make our patients' experience more health-promoting, less stressful and more welcoming. But what cannot be seen or surmised by the patient is even more important. How many medical center employees are assigned to measure surgical excellence compared to how many oversee billing? How many medical center leaders are replaced because the medical outcomes are not satisfactory compared to those replaced because of unsatisfactory financial results? I think it is safe to say that my 8-year-old grandson knows the answer to that.

MAXIMS ON LEADERSHIP

> **Leadership does matter.**

The ill effects of poor leadership, at any level from CEO to department head to housekeeping, insidiously permeate an entire institution. This invariably leads to inefficiency at best, and at worst leads to falling dominoes of lost opportunity or catastrophe. Leadership matters even though its effectiveness may not be apparent in the short term. In fact, it is most effective when its workings and angst are not apparent to most of the people most of the time; in other words, "don't let 'em see you sweat." What makes great leaders is not a secret—they not only have grace under pressure, which means both courage and character, they remain focused on the important aspects of an issue in the midst of chaos, and they repeatedly articulate a consistent, simple public vision. If the troops don't know what is expected of them, what direction is set or what the leader values most, that is the leader's fault.

However, this vision must be backed by public acts, not just words. There are many opportunities to demonstrate one's vision, both subtle and overt. Whom the leader hires, fires and promotes sends the most effective signal, but smaller acts can indirectly express his or her values. Good leaders also usually choose to be judged by, and take satisfaction in, the success of the team members. Top leadership jobs are full-time jobs and must be viewed as a new and specific career choice, not as a minor part-time duty.

> **Leaders are often chosen primarily for characteristics that have little or no correlation with a successful tenure as leader.**

Examples of such criteria include a long bibliography, scientific eminence, institutional longevity, ready availability, a willingness to accept inadequate resources or not rock the boat. Choosing leaders is not a science, but it is surprising how often management skills, interpersonal skills and experience are undervalued. This error is most damaging when recruiting clinical leaders because of the increasing complexity of health care economics and the interface of the academic mission with hospital functions.

What should one look for? It differs, of course, depending on the position. One should ask what critical skills are absolutely essential for that role at that time in that particular setting—there are usually only two or three. It could be scientific taste as much as accomplishment, that is, a keen sense of excellent versus average science as opposed to the ability to run one's own program successfully, or it might be in-the-trenches management experience, inter-personal skills, or the courage to clean house. My point is that we all want superb investigators, teachers and clinicians, preferably able to walk on water, but there are other practical values that are at least as important and often define the success or failure of the leader.

> **For academic leaders, the last 10% of job accomplishment may take as much time as the first 90%, and may not be worth the effort.**

The leader may have exhausted his or her reservoir of moral or financial capital, enthusiasm and will. Moving on to something else may be best for the leader and the institution. This is a hard call for anyone to make, and it is a very lonely decision, but many have made it. My decision to leave St. Jude after 24 years was very difficult, but I thought that after nine years as director, I had accomplished at least 90% of what I would ever do there, no matter how long I stayed. We built new buildings and recruited nine new chairmen and I was afraid I would just be oiling the machine for the rest of my career. That would have been bad for me and, ultimately, for the institution. Which leads to the next maxim.

> **With rare exceptions, the appropriate maximum term for an academic leader/administrator is 10 years, plus or minus 3 years.**

Fresh ideas, energy and resources are needed for vital, creative organizations and it is often easier for a new leader to redress mistakes, adapt and restructure the organization, and clean out deadwood. The number of academic leaders who remain effective, adaptive and unselfish for two decades or more is miniscule compared to those who stay on only because of accumulated power, political maneuvering, or institutional delusion and inertia. In this respect, it is not new space or funds that are at risk; they are comparatively easy for the seasoned leader to continue to obtain. It is scientific creativity, innovation and organizational modification that suffer. I choose about 10 years from simple observation of the academic world.

> **Contrary to the laws of physics in academic institutions, crap flows uphill.**

With any significant problem, error or conflict, the bigger the stink and the more contentious the conflict, the more rapid the uphill rise. Leaders often try to ignore or deflect the unpleasant mess, but the longer it incubates, the harder it will be to sanitize. A keen nose catching a faint whiff early in the process can prevent costly and time-consuming embarrassment. Many leaders do more sniffing above (chairman, dean, trustee) than below, which is where many of the most serious problems arise.

For a really big stink at the highest levels, one must deal with the press. Our instincts in those cases are like those of a child—we think that if we keep it quiet, it will blow over. We naively believe that the patient who suffers a major surgical or chemotherapy error so loves the physician, or the aggrieved faculty member so loves the institution, that they certainly wouldn't want to raise a public fuss or cause unpleasantness. And we believe that if the media learns of it, it will be discreet, or at least wait until one can gather all the facts. Wrong on all counts. If it can hit the fan, it will, and fast. You can count on it. I've been involved in several major institutional miscues in which the muck landed in my lap and in the press. The best approach is get the facts very quickly, inform the Trustees, get the public relations department involved, decide on a course of reparative action and act, all on the first day, if possible. And then prepare to make a statement to the press that is brief and forthcoming. One might get lucky and dodge a bullet, but decisive action is still best.

COMMENTARIES ON LEADERSHIP

What Makes a Great Leader?

Changes in leadership are common at government agencies and the academic medical centers influenced by them. Having observed such changes recently, I have begun to ask myself what makes a good leader of these organizations and, better yet, what makes a great leader.

Leadership matters; it matters a lot. This is so whether the organization is a business, a practice, a hospital, an academic institution or a government agency. Books on business success, including leadership, seem to be everywhere. Typical is the book by Jack Welch, the former CEO of General Electric, which became a best seller. While books on leadership of non-profit organizations, particularly those in health sciences and health care, are almost non-existent, leadership qualities are shared in both for-profit and non-profit venues. So let's review what some gurus of management have had to say on the subject.

One of my favorite sources of business management wisdom is Peter Drucker. This legendary sage understood and clearly described the features of running successful businesses. He is famous for believing that integrity and high ethical standards were central to good business practice because it was the right thing to do, but also because it was good for the long-term health of an organization. Here is an excerpt from his work.

"What would I look for in picking a leader of an institution? First, I would look at what the candidates have done, what their strengths are-- you can only perform with strength---and what have they done with it? Second, I would look at the institution and ask: 'What is the one immediate key challenge?' I would try to match the strength with the needs. Then I would look for integrity. A leader sets an example, especially a strong leader."

Drucker then quotes a famous and successful business leader whom he asked what he looked for in a leader. And the man responded, "I always ask myself, would I want one of my sons to work under that person? If [the leader] is successful... would I want my son to look like that?" Drucker then concludes, "This, I think, is the ultimate question."

He continues, "In human affairs, the distance between the leaders and the average is a constant. If leadership performance is high, the average will go up." And finally, "Effective leaders delegate, but they do not delegate the one thing that will set the standard. They do it."

Another well-known management expert, W. Edwards Deming, also held to this last principle. Deming is best known for being the American consultant who revitalized Japanese industry after the World War II. "It is the responsibility of management to discover the barriers that prevent workers from taking pride in what they do. Rather than helping workers do their job correctly, most supervisors don't know the work they supervise. They have never done the job." Deming goes on to say that such supervisors often use numbers or quotas as the only basis for judgment, without understanding the nature of the work.

The greatest leader in American history was, in my view, Abraham Lincoln. This view was cemented in my opinion by a book that focused on his leadership and political skills and, of course, on aspects of his personal character that shaped the former (*Lincoln: A Life of Purpose and Power*, by Richard Carwardine, Knopf, New York, 2006). Lincoln's integrity, vision and bedrock principles were combined with uncommon political skills acquired in his Illinois years and with a keen sense of public opinion. These enabled him to navigate skillfully the most difficult and treacherous times of our country. He devoured information from all sources and sent aides into the field to obtain first-hand information that helped him make astute strategic decisions. He was an uncommon leader who engaged some political enemies in his administration because he believed they were the best people for the jobs.

In my experience, it has been clear that the ill effects of poor leadership, at any level from CEO to department head to housekeeping, insidiously permeate an entire institution. This invariably leads to inefficiency at best, and at worst leads to falling dominoes of lost opportunity or catastrophe. Effective leadership is often subtle but direct, nuanced but clearly understood.

What makes great leaders is not a secret. They not only have grace under pressure, which means both courage and character, they remain focused on the important aspects of an issue in the midst of chaos. Great leaders repeatedly articulate a consistent, simple public vision by example, conviction and actions. If the troops don't know what is expected of them, what direction is set or what the leader values most, that is the leader's fault.

However, this vision must be backed by public acts, not just words. There are many opportunities to demonstrate one's vision, both subtle and overt. Whom the leader hires, fires and promotes sends the most effective signal, but smaller acts can indirectly express his or her values. Great leaders take satisfaction in the success of team members and try to hire people who are better than they are.

I end with two qualities that help distinguish a great leader from a good leader, especially in the not-for-profit world. First, though he remains confident in his final decisions, he must have humility in sufficient measure to mitigate arrogance and promote active listening to those holding other views. Second, he knows that at some time he will be asked to compromise basic principles. If his values cannot be sustained because of the environment, the great leader may choose to lose favor, be fired, or quit over a key, bedrock principle. If the position or stature or pay means so much to him that the leader will not put his job on the line for such a core value, he is no longer free and has taken a step onto a slippery slope. Great leaders have the mindset of holding core values and principles dear, no matter what the cost.

Understanding Effective Leadership

Trying to understand leadership, good and bad, has been an endlessly fascinating journey for me. And I am not alone. The shelves in the business section at Barnes and Noble are filled with books on the subject and airport concessions, even in smaller airports, always have such books. The Harvard Business Review reliably prints many articles, universities offer continuing education courses, and celebrities give well-paid lectures on leadership. Why is the subject so popular? The answer is easy: because leadership is difficult and because leadership is so important to any enterprise.

A parenthetic note of caution here about business books: I have read my share and found the majority to be useless; they are filled with simplistic nostrums, are endlessly repetitive, and have an almost total dependence on anecdotes (case studies), which by their nature are totally retrospective and uncontrolled. Only a small percentage of books provide an enlightening synthesis or novel viewpoints, so caveat emptor.

In my own case, an interest in the qualities of effective leaders has been greatly intensified beyond sporadic reading by my own experience as a leader of academic programs and hospitals and through my consulting work, which provides opportunities to examine in detail the work and effectiveness of many leaders in health care.

In an earlier essay I described what some experts believe makes a great leader, or rather, what kind of performance and outcome is apparent in very successful leaders. This is an important distinction. It is much easier to identify an effective leader after the fact than before or during his or her tenure. This raises interesting questions, such as: Are leaders made or born? Can someone be taught to be an effective leader? Can one identify an effective leader beforehand? Are all effective leaders "successful?" I hope to shed a bit of light on these issues from the literature and personal experience.

Are leaders born? Yes, partly. I agree with Bill George, a former corporate CEO. In his book, *True North: Discover Your Authentic Leadership*, he expresses in several ways that the core characteristics of leadership, the soul of leadership, cannot be taught. I have come to believe that what is true for most skillful activities is also true for leadership. Not only is one's DNA a major influence, but George points out that personal crises and other life experiences early in life and later also prepare one to be an effective leader.

Although I loved the game, no matter how hard I tried, I could never have been a competitive college football player. I was the wrong size and shape, terribly slow, and had other interests that were more important to me. A friend once told me of a conversation he had with a CEO of a large corporation. He asked the CEO how he could tell if a candidate was likely to be an effective leader. He replied, "Simple, I just asked them what they did in high school." He was making a point that the signs of an aptitude for leadership show up early.

Can one teach effective leadership? Only partly and only if the basic soul of leadership is already there, I believe. One can be taught certain techniques and skills through mentoring and graduated experience. But that is a refinement of the basic foundation of good instincts about human nature, character, ambition and self-confidence. I also believe one can teach, or try to teach, a potential leader that unless he/she gets pleasure out of the success and glory that were due in large part to his efforts, a leadership position may not be a good choice, no matter what other talents he possesses.

Can one identify an effective leader beforehand? This is very difficult and the typical search process often fails to identify the right leader for the specific job. In my view, the best predictor of an effective leader is evidence of effective leadership in the past. This seems to be a Catch 22: "I don't know if you will be an effective leader unless you have already been an effective leader. How can one become an effective leader if one never gets the chance?" But this is not as dumb as it sounds. If someone has had experience as a leader, even in a voluntary or relatively minor position, it usually means that the person wanted to be a leader and went after the job, or was recognized by others as someone they would like as their leader. If he/she were successful in that role, that provides a degree of greater security in the evaluation.

In my personal experience, there are two top reasons for the failure of leaders. First, a candidate is hired for the wrong reasons, e.g. an outstanding scientist is hired to be chairman of a department or a dean primarily because of a long bibliography and an expansive CV. These are poor indicators of an aptitude for leadership, yet are often the most powerful influence on the decision to hire. Second, the candidate likes the position for its stature and power, but doesn't really like (or understand) the job of leadership. This type often is just a boss or even a bully, but not an effective leader that leads the team to perform at its best.

Are all effective leaders successful? No. This is one of the great faults of business books on leadership. Too often the only measure of an effective corporate leader is an increase in market share or stock price. In academia, it is grants obtained or papers published. Books don't sell if they describe the leader who, despite seemingly insurmountable obstacles, managed to bring his so-so team to a much higher level of performance than expected, but not to the top of his field. Or the leader who inherited a staff ill-fitted for the job, but was able to rearrange the workforce and workflow to help them perform at their very best. The athletic directors of college sports know this well. They often hire a coach who has turned a chronically losing team at a second or third tier sports college into one that wins half its games. They recognize the coaching talent despite the mediocre player talent.

In summary, effective leaders are born with an innate aptitude that is shaped and grown by life experiences and refined by mentorship and experience; all three are necessary. Although not fail-safe, one makes a better bet on a prospective leader who has a record of successful leadership in the past, no matter at what level. Finally, excellent and effective leaders may not be judged successful by the world's standards, but they may have done an excellent job with the resources and conditions provided – and they usually know that in their hearts.

Boss, Manager, or Leader?

In recent weeks I have visited and spoke at a number of academic institutions. My agenda generally included private and small group meetings with senior faculty, junior faculty and trainees. I am struck by how often I am asked questions about specific issues that we in academia or the practice of medicine must deal with. The top three issues for those in positions of authority concerned: 1) personnel problems; 2) personnel problems; and 3) personnel problems. As a friend once told me, "this job would be easy if I didn't have to deal with people."

On the other hand, my discussions with those that have no authority (junior or mid-career faculty and fellows) consisted mainly of questions concerning career choices and navigating through the organization. I believe I benefit as much or more than they do from the exchange because every session has offered a viewpoint or an issue in a slightly different light, thus refining my own thoughts and leading me to read up on certain topics.

This time the rumination led to exploring the different styles employed by those in positions of authority. The words "boss," "manager," and "leader" are often used interchangeably, e.g. in casual conversation the boss is the top person in the workplace hierarchy who often has the ability to hire and fire individuals.

But I would like to refine the usual all-purpose definitions as a means of exploring the nuances of people and their behavior in those hierarchical positions. But listing such a hierarchy is not entirely objective, of course; experience plays a large role in judging authority when one gets older, and one's own rank in an organization colors one's perception of persons in authority.

For me "the boss" is a very powerful, largely dictatorial, judgmentally mysterious, and unpredictable character. He is someone to be feared more than respected. He is more likely to lose his temper and threaten violence (rarely physical, but by other means such as demotion or assigning the worst tasks). The archetype of "the boss" in my life was the foreman of a construction crew that I worked with for three summers. The crew of laborers worked very hard for long hours in the hot, humid Chicago summers with a 30-minute break for lunch. We dug ditches, lugged 50-70 pound wooden forms for the concrete curbs and sidewalks, backfilled the forms and loaded the equipment on trucks. There was no room for innovation or improvements of the processes; they were fixed in concrete. At the end of summer I was in the best physical shape of my life. The job paid relatively well, but there was an air of fear at the worksite and we always were alert to where the foreman was. I have had other bosses, but none as threatening as the foreman.

The men that typify the "manager" for me were those with that title at the A&P supermarkets that I worked at during high school. They assigned work, checked progress, occasionally relieved cashiers (in those days all were women). They had the power to hire and fire, but they didn't really scare anyone; they were largely benign. Some were collegial and personable, some were all business, but they all went about their jobs in workmanlike fashion. Most worked their way up the system from stocking shelves to running the produce department and finally, manager. They didn't inspire loyalty or admiration or dazzle anyone with their brilliance or imagination.

The "leader" is a person who inspires the troops to follow his or her plan and exemplifies important values such as integrity, candor, decisiveness, and fairness. The leader may have a touch of charisma and at least seem approachable, a value that makes him or her a bit more like the rest of us. He or she has a clear and well-articulated vision, an essential factor so all the troops are, or can be, on the same page. A leader has many of the skills of the boss and the manager, but sees the bigger picture, has more patience for success and takes pleasure in seeing individuals who work in his organization become successful and rewarded with accolades or lucre. The leader get his kicks out of seeing others do well...which, of course, makes him/her look good because he/she is the leader of a successful team.

For me Dr. Donald Pinkel, the first director of St. Jude Children's Research Hospital, typifies a leader as I have defined it. He was the brains of our pediatric oncology program but was very generous in giving us the opportunity to share the credit with him. He put us forward for speaking engagements and as representatives of the program. He was charismatic and eminently approachable. But he also was firm in his core beliefs about ethical standards and our societal responsibilities as a children's research institute. One example: We became engaged in nutritional studies of poor children in our Memphis community and we helped obtain surplus food from the U.S. Department of Agriculture for those children in need. Pinkel took heat from some St. Jude trustees and faculty for these efforts, but he prevailed and Dr. Paul Zee, who was the leader of the studies, was asked to testify before The U.S. Congress on our program. Zee demonstrated that nutritional status influenced school performance; this would surprise no one today, but in the maelstrom of the 1960s, this was important ammunition for like-minded people. That effort helped the government establish the hugely successful national WIC program, The Special Supplemental Nutrition Program for Women, Infants and Children, which distributes FDA surplus food commodities to those in need.

My conclusion from these many years of experience is the following: there are many bosses and managers in most organizations at all levels from CEO on down, but there are relatively few leaders. You are blessed when you serve a true leader because he/she can help you by example to become a leader yourself. That may be the greatest gift of leadership.

The Five Deadly Sins of Leadership

This essay describes the condensed wisdom of Peter Drucker, an icon of business management wisdom. It became clear when reading his works that the key values he describes can be applied to leadership in the "healthcare industry," from the Food and Drug Administration, the National Cancer Institute and pharmaceutical companies to academic medical centers and oncology practices. The "sins" of leadership described below can be seen in the non-profit as well as the for-profit industry, and in professional businesses such as academic departments and private medical practices.

Drucker wrote an article for the *Wall Street Journal* in 1993 entitled, "The Five Deadly Business Sins." It was reprinted in the 21 October 2005 issue of the Journal following Drucker's death. What prompted the article was the downward slide in the few years before of once-dominant businesses such as General Motors, IBM and Sears. He believed that each was guilty of at least one of five business sins. Some of these come uncomfortably close to describing recognizable "sins" in the oncology world. Keep in mind that Drucker calls these "sins" because they are bad for business, not necessarily for one's soul or moral compass (though Drucker has made the argument that good business practices and high ethical standards are often aligned).

Sin #1: Worship of high profit margins and "premium pricing." Drucker says this is the most common of the deadly business sins and offers several examples. Xerox invented the copier but kept adding features to increase the profit margin. But most consumers needed a plain copier at reasonable cost; when Canon brought one out it proceeded to dominate the U.S. market for years. General Motors neglected the market for smaller, more fuel-efficient cars even after the oil crisis of the 1970s, consciously ceding that market to Volkswagen and Japanese carmakers. Only after the latter controlled that large market did GM try to respond, but GM remains behind 30 years later because the Japanese cars have been of consistently higher quality.

The pharmaceutical company functions as a legal monopoly with a new drug because of patent protection and will charge "what the market will bear." But is that bad business? Drucker would say yes. Xerox and GM made billions of dollars early in their downward spiral, but the market eventually caught up with them and we saw the consequences three decades later. Xerox is now a minor player in copiers and at that time there was talk, only half-jokingly, that Toyota might buy GM.

And we can point to ourselves for what has happened to oncology practices, both academic and community-based. While chemotherapy revenues were soaring, reaching an average of 65%-85% of all revenues, there was no agitation to improve the paltry reimbursement for seeing and managing the patient, so practices became dependent on that single source of revenue. The Medicare Modernization Act of 2003 severely reduced the profit from the resale of drugs so many patients are being sent to hospitals for their chemotherapy, especially from small practices, which have been the hardest hit. And larger practices are scrambling to reorganize into buying consortiums and to own lucrative diagnostic or radiation therapy facilities to make up for the income "shortfall." The key difference between the cancer industry on the one hand and Xerox and GM on the other are that patients are not machine products. So the consequences of charging desperate patients tens of thousands of dollars for minimally effective cancer treatment are exponentially greater and, I would argue, more relevant to the cancer industry, not less. There is a strong moral-ethical as well as a business case for addressing these "sins."

Sin #2: Mispricing a new product by charging "what the market will bear." This is simply an extension of Sin #1. Drucker offers an interesting example of an American company that did it right. DuPont has remained on top of the synthetic fiber industry. When DuPont developed nylon, it priced the patented product at the price they would have to charge in five years to stay competitive. They sacrificed short-term profits for long term stability and, in the long run, greater profits.

Sin #3: Reliance on cost-driven pricing. Most companies total up their costs and add a profit to arrive at the sales price. They do this because "we must recover our costs and make a profit." But the market often changes due to competition, government regulation or unforeseen production or distribution problems. So the company then must cut the price or redesign the product.

Drucker says the alternative and wiser approach is the opposite: "price-driven costing." That is, price a product or service to what the market is willing to pay and control the costs to fit the price. If one takes this approach, the competition will have a hard time undercutting the price and grabbing market share. This would be a hard sell at every level of the cancer industry. Certainly, the NCI finds itself facing serious reductions in research grants because the Congress believes it isn't doing a good job. Whatever the merits of Congress's judgment, the recent large investment in nanotechnology, proteomics and bioinformatics at the cost of creative research demonstrates either NCI's lack of planning for what "the market will bear," or a misunderstanding of how research progress is and always has been made: by a pool of creative individual investigators that teach the next generation of creative investigators. Each is a potentially fatal error for the future of biomedical research.

Sin #4: Slaughtering tomorrow's opportunity on the altar of yesterday. IBM brought out the first personal computer, but consciously ceded that new and growing business to Apple and then many others to focus on its lucrative mainframe business. It is said that IBM forbade its PC salesmen to sell to its mainframe customers. It forced the development of PC clones which businesses wanted. IBM recently sold even its successful laptop business to Lenovo, a Chinese company, and has changed its business model to feature consulting.

The cancer industry (all of us in research, production and

care) is in danger of making the same error. Reliance and continued investment in marginally–effective diagnostics and therapies at enormous cost to patients, the public and to the government keep the industry profitable. But one can argue that this failure by the industry to call into question the true value of these approaches for general use-- proton-beam therapy, expensive targeted drugs (When did we ever give drugs we believed were not targeted?) for lung cancer that extend life on average only a few weeks is the same as IBM sticking with the mainframes.

Sin #5: Feeding problems and starving opportunities. This is a variant of Sin #4. Drucker illustrates this with an anecdote. He says he always asks new clients who their best-performing people are and where they are assigned. In almost all cases they are assigned to problems—old products, fading lines of business, old technology. He then asks, "Who takes care of opportunities?" Their development is usually left to less able performers who are often left to fend for themselves. He believes Sears has been doing this for years. He said GE on the other hand "gets rid of all old business, even if profitable, that do not offer long-range growth and the opportunity for the company to be number one or two world-wide."

The biomedical research community of the U.S., funded largely by the NIH, is number one in the world. I would argue it is because its main focus has been its priority of supporting research project grants that are competitively awarded. Although large-scale projects such as nanotechnology, bioinformatics and proteomics have merit, I question whether the NCI can ever be number one or number two in these areas. It has little strength in technology development. And such expenditures come at the extremely high cost of squeezing many scientists, especially the up-and-comers, out of the business. The result: the pay lines for investigator-initiated grants are shrinking toward single digits.

Peter Drucker's words should give us pause about the direction of the NCI and the whole cancer business. Admittedly, it is difficult to see how individuals can address these issues. It will require an open-minded leadership at NCI to invite an analysis of its portfolio by competent extramural scientists and clinical investigators. If the next director and the Congress continue in the current direction, a decade or two from now the U.S. will no longer be number one in cancer research and, by extension, biomedical research. Just keep in mind the letters SGX—Sears, GM and Xerox.

Pruning the Rosebush

My gardening is limited by my impatience and my unwillingness to spend hours crouching or on my knees. OK, so I'm lazy. But there are some aspects of maintaining plants that I do willingly, almost instinctively. One of these is pruning rose bushes. To have the best blossoms for the longest time, one must have removed dead wood and, once blooming begins, one must remove spent blossoms. Both actions take little time and stimulate new growth. One is tempted to leave a blossom that is well past its prime, but retains some color and scent; I have done this many times. But when I do that, I find that I have reduced the bush's productivity and diminished its overall appearance and the pleasure it brings. So I prune without remorse.

Although much more difficult, pruning is just as necessary in organizations. The most common reasons for firing an individual in professional life are (1) a lack of performance or productivity, (2) his/her negative impact on the performance or productivity of colleagues or (3) a clash of his/her personality or values with the culture of the workplace. Some organizations fire too readily, but the vast majority fire too little or too late, especially in academia and government. Tenure, legal or practical, is often blamed for not firing incompetents, and with good reason (full disclosure: I am opposed to tenure in professional schools).

But more often, the incompetent or destructive individual is left in place because the leader doesn't want the unpleasantness and hassle of removing the individual, the culture of the organization frowns on it, or someone fears a lawsuit. One approach is to try to transfer or hide the individual in hopes that will contain the damage, but that seldom works because a determined malcontent can always find ways to hurt the organization. Even more important is the message sent to all the "good" employees: we won't get rid on an incompetent, so you work harder to make up for his low productivity and put up with his behavior. This is not a morale booster.

For most of us in leadership positions, firing people is the hardest part of the job; there are few who take pleasure in wielding such power. Unlike roses, one is dealing with human beings who have families and responsibilities. Depending on the circumstances, firing a professional will certainly harm his or her career development and, in some extreme cases, may even end it. There are rare circumstances when it is relatively easy to fire a professional, such as cases of fraud, theft or other major unethical or criminal behavior. But even then, one is left with a feeling of profound sadness.

There are two main types of "firing," firing someone from an "appointed" position or from employment altogether. Appointed positions in academia include dean, chairman of a department, division head or cancer center director. In those cases, the person may be fired from the appointed job, but retain an often tenured professorship. In community practice it includes medical director at a hospital or an administrative role in the practice itself. Being fired from an appointed position will hurt one's ego, but it doesn't usually threaten one's livelihood. Separating one from the organization is a different matter.

Firing someone from employment may appear to be pretty clear-cut for most individuals, but it isn't that easy, especially when dealing with professionals. In academia one must deal with tenure, in private practice with partnerships and in all types of employment with contracts, grievances, EEOC issues, etc.

So it is always a good idea to go to great lengths to minimize the likelihood of firing an individual. In addition to the usual screening and obtaining references, I am a believer in screening professional candidates by phone call. I believe the future boss or peer should talk to people from the candidate's current institution(s) or practice(s). This is especially effective if one knows the person called. Written recommendations are often formulaic and not very useful, though a skillfully written letter to an experienced recruiter can implicitly reveal a great deal. People are often much more open on a phone call and will say things or hint at things they would not put in writing. I have been dumbfounded by the frequency of individuals, both high achievers and low, being hired by another organization without any request for recommendations.

But despite all precautions, everyone in a leadership position will surely face the prospect of firing someone. Of course, it should never be done lightly, but when the productivity of the organization is severely or chronically compromised, the individual should be nudged out if possible, or thrown out if necessary. That is a leader's responsibility—to get best available people and to create an environment conducive to fulfilling their potential and the organization's.

There is a circumstance that requires a different approach; I call it the "bad fit." In my experience, this has been the most common situation I faced. An employee may work hard, have good values and get along with colleagues but is not right for the organization. The organization's culture may have well-established expectations beyond the capability of the individual no matter how hard he works; a smart, hard-working individual who everybody likes who just can't cut it. His work lacks something, such as imagination or sufficient detail in their research, always being a step behind clinically, or an inability to write up his work. Whatever it is, it is just a bad fit for that environment.

For a bad fit, the solution is to help them find a more suitable environment. Be very clear that they must go, but give them time to find another position, coach them on where to look, make some calls for them. They may not thank you for any help you provide, after all, you are firing them. But you will be able to sleep better and you can provide an honest reference, e.g., "he works hard, but the chemistry here just didn't work out—it is my fault as much as his."

Pruning a rose bush is necessary for the greatest achievement of its beauty and productivity. Firing a person occasionally--one hopes rarely—is necessary for the health and productivity of an organization. It should be a last resort after every attempt has been made to save the situation, but when all else fails it becomes the sad duty of the leader, for the good of all in the organization.

Desire and Talent
....

I have been in love with Euterpe for many years, but she does not love me. I have courted her and tried to please her. I have looked to those that she favors to understand how I might receive her graces, graces that would bring my life joy and fulfillment. But despite my passionate desire, she still ignores me.

Euterpe is the Greek Muse of lyric poetry and music. The ancient Greeks believed that the Muses had the power, by bestowing their graces, to inspire poets to write beautifully and musicians to compose and play memorable music. I love poetry and music and have tried my hand at creating both. But I have failed. I enjoy reading poetry and listening to music and can appreciate the difference between the excellent, good and mediocre in each genre. But despite trying over many, many years, I cannot write good, much less excellent, poetry. And the only musical instruments I can play are the radio and the iPod.

There are many reasons that might explain this failure: a lack of early exposure, inadequate formal training, my failure to work hard enough, or a lack of perseverance. But being honest with myself, I must face the fact that I just don't have the talent, I don't have that creative spark for poetry and music.

It is painful to face that conclusion, but I do not lose sleep over it...and that in itself speaks volumes; a creative poet or musician would lose sleep. I don't lose sleep because I can derive considerable satisfaction and enjoyment from being a recreational poet or reading outstanding poetry, likewise for painting or music. (Well, maybe not a musician...my wife and I probably have the worst singing voices on earth; our birthday gift to one another each year is to promise NOT to sing "Happy Birthday.")

It has occurred to me that this scene is replayed over and over in our society not just in poetry and music, but also in our everyday jobs. The single most common error of leadership in my own world of medicine and academic life is placing someone in a job for which they have no talent. Here are a few examples; they are composites of many I have witnessed.

1. An outstanding scientist is appointed chairman of a research department because of an impressive CV and a million dollars in grants. He desires the job because of its power and prestige. However, he has no interpersonal skills and little interest in nurturing and developing the department's faculty. He often views trainees and junior faculty as slave labor to promote his own career, providing them little opportunity to eventually become independent investigators. After 5 or 10 years, he may have been elected to the National Academy of Sciences, but he did not perform as a department chairman because he alone was the department and if he left, there would be no department to speak of. He was the wrong person for the job.

2. A physician-scientist is appointed chair of a medical department because he got his tickets punched along the academic toll road. He attended elite schools and training programs; co-authored papers in the *New England Journal of Medicine* and *Science*; was elected a member of the Society for Clinical Investigation; sat on panels for reviewing NIH grant proposals; became head of an academic division; and was elected an officer in his specialty or subspecialty society. He is a skilled academic politician who is appointed department chairman and spends a great deal of his time honing those skills and avoiding "bad marks" that might prevent him from becoming a dean someday, the next step on the toll-road.

But he has no strategic vision and will not take a stand on principle if it means he might annoy someone up the power ladder or lose some of his own power, so he (and his department with him) ambles along in mediocrity. Because of his political skills, his ineffectiveness as a leader is not appreciated (or more accurately, not faced) by his superiors until damage is done and there is a substantial and irreversible loss of opportunity and a waste of departmental resources. He was the wrong person for the job.

3. A cancer center director is appointed because he has worked in a very good cancer center and is a respected subspecialist. But he has never had the responsibility of leading anything. He is given the task of running one of the most complex organizations in academia while having no experience, training or innate talent that would help him address the multitude of hurdles, the incessant bargaining, raising money, and dealing with whining and under-performing members.

He lacks the organizational skills to delegate appropriately, to articulate a simple, clear vision of where the center is headed, and he can't manage his way out of a paper bag. The end game for this type is at times a retreat into his laboratory or clinic, sometimes hoarding resources for his personal program or that of close friends in the cancer center. That is not the worst of it; despite the widespread belief, sometimes for years, that he is a loser and ill-fitted to the job, his superiors don't remove him. The reasons are many, including the expense of attracting a new director, a low opinion of the cancer center concept, or just plain paralysis.

4. The final example is not from academia, but in the private practice sector. The leader of a community oncology group is a skilled entrepreneur. His ability to generate revenue is amazing: he installs software to identify the most lucrative chemotherapy regimen for a cancer and buys radiation therapy and diagnostic equipment (and the physicians who operate them) as an investment for the practice to hedge against falling chemotherapy reimbursement. He brings in bushels of money and makes each practitioner rich with incomes exceeding $1 million annually. He is a king respected not for his clinical skills, commitment to quality improvement, or research expertise, but for making money.

These activities may be legal, but they have an insidious side effect that may kill the soul of the practice: the practitioners learn to live up to their new windfall and eventually are addicted to or trapped by it. They are left with no palatable option except doing anything possible to sustain that income. Any attempt to take the practice in a risky new direction or to install expensive, but non-profitable, equipment or services paid from practice earnings (e.g. electronic medical record, a serious quality improvement program) is viewed with suspicion or outright derision. The practitioners become venture capitalists that lose sight of or laugh at the idea that, at its best, practicing medicine is a privilege and a noble calling. Thus, the leader is "successful" and has surrounded himself with those who learn to view success only in monetary rather than medical terms.

In these examples, the leader has talent, but the talent has little to do with the job of leading a professional organization, of professing its highest avowed standards. If I write poetry that is bad and I continue writing, knowing full well that I have no talent, I have hurt no one nor have I violated a trust. If I lead a professional organization and have no talent for that job, I have adversely affected many lives and the institution by setting a bad example and perpetuating a culture that accepts mediocrity as an acceptable norm. Anyone entrusted to make these appointments has made bad choices now and then (I have made my share). But the unwillingness to take often-painful corrective action for the good of the organization (and often for the good of the ill-suited person) compounds the error ten-fold and perpetuates a downward spiral.

There is no Muse to inspire gifted leadership and management talent, no matter how strong our desire.

MAXIMS ON RECRUITING

> **In recruiting, first class people recruit first class people; second class people recruit third class people.**

Some hesitate to recruit a person who is smart enough and ambitious enough to compete with them. Others want a position filled at any cost because of "desperate" clinical need or other institutional pressures. If that approach continues for long, the third class people will eventually dominate in numbers and influence and ultimately chase away any first rate people that remain. I've hired my share of bad recruits. When I was younger, I just suffered with the mistake and groused about dishonest references. Later in my career, I realized that everyone will inevitably make recruiting mistakes and it is wisest to lance the boil as soon as possible. I've had to fire a number of people that I hired or inherited, including several chairmen. In my experience, the following sequence of action worked best. First make certain of the facts, looking especially for a pattern of unacceptable or unproductive behavior. The immediate superior should always give the bad news in person and in private. And, if possible, he should have prepared a reasonably dignified way out for the individual. This is difficult and very unpleasant work, but I learned that letting it fester was much worse for the institution and for the individual.

> **Personal attitude and team compatibility is grossly under-rated in faculty recruiting.**

"Always recruit the best athlete" or, in this case, "the best scientist," is a stupid over-simplification. A faculty member may be very productive personally, but create an atmosphere that reduces the productivity of everyone else. A small, but distressing, number of academic programs have a stifling air of distrust and scientific secrecy leading to competing factions and an enormous waste of energy. These programs tend to attract others covered with negative ions and a purely self-serving attitude – they deserve each other.

> **Recruits bring a culture as well as expertise with them.**

A recruiter overlooks and under-weights this maxim at his/ her peril. A candidate who has been in a particular work environment for a long time may have that culture engrained in him or her and may not adapt easily to a different culture. For example, candidates who have been in government for their formative and productive years may not find it easy to understand and deal with a new set of cultural standards and professional expectations in the private sector

Moving from a research institute to a university proved to be difficult in my own career. University culture was far more conservative, slow-moving and risk-averse than I had been accustomed to, and far more dependent on consensus and a multi-layered hierarchy for decisions and movement. I have seen difficulties with the reverse move, as well. To be sure, some eventually adapt well to the new culture. But especially for managers and other leaders, I have seen stormy cultural adaptations doom their effectiveness.

> **The longer and more detailed the written offer to a new faculty recruit, the more likely both sides will end up unhappy.**

A two- or three-page letter spelling out the specific expectations and benchmarks of accountability usually suffice. But I've known of offer letters that ran 20 or 25 pages. This starts a relationship on a note of distrust, which will be hard to shake off later. Lawyers may become involved, a catastrophe for all. Further, this attitude may spread to other faculty, current and future. On the other hand, institutions or leaders that earn a reputation for failing to deliver on promises of resources deserve distrust, but written commitments are worthless in that case anyway. If a candidate feels he or she must have a long and detailed offer letter because of distrust, it would be better not to take the job. Trust that one's boss or bosses will act in one's best interest is probably the single most important factor in job satisfaction, especially in the first few years. It is the recruit's responsibility to talk to as many as possible of the boss's current and former colleagues to gauge that trust. Whom to talk to varies depending on rank; for example, a post-doc should talk to current and former post-docs, an assistant professor to assistants, and so forth. There is an exception: It doesn't matter who candidates for deanships talk to— the fact that they are considering becoming a dean already shows a flair for adventure and self-delusion, so evaluations by others aren't very influential in the decision.

> **Faculty fired for incompetence will almost always land a better job at higher pay.**

I can hear you thinking that this maxim is crazy, but I have seen and experienced this many times. There are two possible reasons for this incredible irony. First, the firing party has demonstrated, at least in this instance, strong leadership, high standards and guts. I believe that coming from such an upstanding laboratory, program or institution is quite helpful on the incompetent's CV. Second, the person may be in the wrong type of job and dismissal provides an opportunity move to a better position, a more appropriate setting, and/or higher pay. When he lands the nice new job, though, I assure you that his former boss will certainly not be thanked for forcing the job change. The first faculty member I had to fire was a friend and colleague, but it was clear he wouldn't make it as a senior clinical investigator in his chosen area. He landed a job in a medical school where research wasn't required. He was very successful at raising the quality of patient care and teaching students and house staff. Another was a scientist, a 10-year employee, whose contract wasn't renewed because it was clear he wasn't going to succeed as an independent investigator. He went to a small biotech company where he flourished and, incidentally, made a pile of dough. It simply fit his skills and temperament better.

COMMENTARIES ON RECRUITING

Judging Personality and Character

We are pretty good at judging someone's scientific productivity because we have a written record of publications, grants and honors. But we have a paucity of methods of judging someone's personality and character, particularly someone we have not worked with directly. Personality is the pattern of traits that helps define a person, including character, behavior, and temperament.

Along with wisdom, strength of character is a premier quality one would like in a colleague or friend. Character embodies honesty, candor, sensitivity, and gentleness. A wise person once said that character is reflected by what you do when no one is watching.

Judging personality and character is a practical necessity when one is hiring, partnering or considering employment. Taking a job in a very good institution or practice can be a nightmare if one's boss or colleagues are of poor character. Even one toxic personality can poison the atmosphere of an entire working environment. We can ask colleagues who know a person well ("How is he to work with?"), but we then must be able to judge the character of the one who is providing the information because his opinion may be clouded by jealousy, provincialism, or other personal matters.

So I have developed a shorthand tool for classifying personality and character in a person. It isn't perfect, but determining where an individual likely would fit can be revealing.

The method I use is imagining the person in a particular environment and asking myself how I would feel about it.

Desert Island My most stringent test is how I would feel if the person in question and I were shipwrecked and ended up on a desert island together, just the two of us. Would he be trustworthy and look out for my interests along with his? Could I depend on him to pull his share of the workload? How would we get along in that stressful situation? I have a number of friends and family members who would pass that test because of their character and because of other qualities, such as temperament, generosity, and good humor.

For this test, one must know and interact with the person over time. Job candidates previously unknown to me could not make the grade. Colleagues and bosses, friends and acquaintances can be assessed.

Daily Interdependent Colleague This next level, not as stringent as the first, imagines what it would be like to deal with this individual on a daily basis and be dependent on his or her actions and behavior. This test can be applied to anyone and often must be made with little information concerning character, such as when recruiting a person to work in one's lab or clinical group. One can get glimpses of personality and character in social situations such as recruiting dinners; sometimes a couple of glasses of wine work better than water-boarding at revealing personal traits.

As a candidate being considered for a position, one's immediate boss is the most important factor in one's success and satisfaction with the position. Is this a person who will be open, helpful and trustworthy? Is he likely to keep his word? Does he have a healthy sense of humor? Is he respected and liked by his current colleagues?

Project Collaborator This measure is one more step less stringent because the association is limited to a specific project and, perhaps, to a limited time span. You won't be living with this person every day. Nonetheless, some of the same issues come up. Will he deliver his part of the work in a timely manner? Can I trust his data or experiment or his clinical acumen? In the end, will I be able to sign off on our combined work without hesitation?

Nice Guy, But... One of the most ironic judgments one can make about a person is, "He is a nice guy, but..." This means he is not personally offensive and may be an excellent social dinner companion. But he is a bad fit in the position, a painfully slow worker, simply not bright enough or aggressive enough for the job, or doesn't function well as part of a team. This is sad because one often likes the person and tries to find the right niche, but he just fails to click because his personality profile doesn't fit the position.

South End of a Horse The SEH can be bright, ambitious, and productive, but a complete jerk that annoys and frustrates everyone around him, often reducing the productivity of his colleagues. This is a guy that tempers one's enthusiasm about heading off to work in the morning. He is always pushing the envelope of what constitutes a pleasant working environment. Propriety, graciousness, candor, and kindness are not a part of his personality. He is socially toxic. This is the guy who causes many to roll their eyes at his behavior. This is partly due to an outsized ego; if he were a child one would call him a spoiled brat. There are often enough hints before he is hired to prevent his employment.

The more difficult situation is if the SEH turns out to be the boss. One is forced to put up with this behavior, at least for a time. This trap is even worse if he heads a prestigious department or section. One must always distinguish between the prestige of the organization with one's own. Building one's own career can be very difficult, irrespective of the reputation of the boss or organization, if an SEH boss compromises one's productivity or job satisfaction.

The Predator This person is usually successful as measured by grants or clinical revenues or even scientific achievement. But he or she acts like an alpha male gorilla by trying to control and dominate an entire organization. He marshals an outsized share of available resources and never seems to have enough. He often develops a quasi- independent organization with little or no concern for the larger organization or other departments.

The classic example in a medical school is the surgeon with a lucrative practice group who develops his own independent empire that may include a fund-raising apparatus, a public relations effort, and an independent clinical trials office, all essentially separate from the school. This person often creates a powerful vortex in any committee meeting that sucks discourse and civility out of the air to better put forward his own agenda.

University hospitals love this guy because his group brings in patients and money. Some deans love this guy because he is well known nationally. Members of other departments often view him as a predator that eats up a giant share of the resources and has an excessive impact on strategic decisions. There are two strategic flaws in this setup. If the guy gets hit by a car, his program usually dies because he is the star and there can be no other equivalent star in his program. And this model allows for teamwork only when it is of the most benefit to the predator; that wears thin pretty fast. These people are easy to identify and should be avoided if their activities impact one's own.

Clearly, this method of assessment is idiosyncratic and imperfect, but it provides me with a framework of how to deal with people. We all must judge and the sooner we figure it out, the better off we will be. But also keep in mind that people do (very rarely) change, so one must be prepared to re-evaluate from time to time.

Intelligence and Wisdom

In a recent article in the New York Times (7 December 2008), Frank Rich commented on the cabinet selections of Barack Obama. He pointed out the gold-plated academic pedigrees and intellectual horsepower of the economic team—mainly

Lawrence Summers, Timothy Geithner and Robert Rubin — and expressed concern that this selection echoed the choices of John F. Kennedy for many of the top jobs in his administration. The latter group was described in David Halberstam book, *The Best and The Brightest*, an indictment of the "hubristic J.F.K. team that would ultimately mire America in Viet Nam."

Before his death Halberstam commented that the book's title had entered the language, but not quite as he had hoped. "It is often misused," he wrote, "failing to carry the tone or irony that the original intended." Rich explains that "the phrase, in its original coinage, was meant to strike a sardonic, not a flattering note." In the Kennedy administration, McGeorge Bundy, Walt Rostow, and Robert McNamara were youthful prodigies, the smartest everywhere they went, resulting in platinum-plated resumes – Groton, Yale, Harvard, MIT as students and academic leaders.

In the book, Halberstam makes a clear case that the impressive intellectual horsepower was poisoned by hubris and arrogance that led to the colossal screw-up of Viet Nam, which "would destroy the presidency of Lyndon Johnson and inflict grave national wounds that are only now healing."

Halberstam commented that his favorite passage in the book recalled that Lyndon Johnson, after the first J.F.K. cabinet meeting, raved about the intellect of Kennedy's choices to Sam Rayburn, then Speaker of the House from Texas and Johnson's mentor. Rayburn responded, "You may be right, and they may be every bit as intelligent as you say, but I'd feel a whole lot better about them if just one of them had run for sheriff once."

For Halberstam this story underlined the weakness of the Kennedy team: "the difference between intelligence and wisdom, between the abstract quickness and verbal facility which the team exuded, and true wisdom, which is the product of hard-won, often bitter experience."

As I read this story I nodded my head in recognition because I have seen this error made many times in my career... and I have made this error myself. The use of intellect and academic accomplishment as the dominant, even sole, criterion for leadership positions in the absence of a serious assessment of wisdom, leadership skills, and humility has often led to disasters, major and minor, in academia, industry, the public sector, and in healthcare.

In my own career world, the most common error is recruiting a department chairman based almost exclusively on a sparkling C.V. that includes prestigious awards and lots of grants. The assumption is made that if that person can organize an effective research program, he or she could easily run a department. Sometimes that is correct, but when it is not, the fallout does harm to the institution and to those in the ranks who are dependent on the wisdom of the leader to provide guidance and an environment conducive to achievement and a reasonable level of comity.

A similar and even more devastating error is the recruitment of a chairman with credentials as described above who is put in charge of a clinical department but has no substantive interest in or contemporary experience in clinical medicine. The grants look good on the dean's report card, but indifference or downright disrespect for the clinical faculty is transmitted wordlessly by actions, often subtle, that convey those feelings. Arrogance and hubris are easily detected. This atmosphere depresses morale, and in my own area of oncology, that is especially serious. We oncologist face enough factors that chip away at morale without more coming from our bosses.

But the wisdom Halberstam describes is not so easy to define and is especially difficult to detect prospectively. Here is a definition of wisdom from my dictionary: "The ability to discern or judge what is true, right or lasting; insight; common sense; good judgment." To some extent the terms wisdom and intelligence have similar and overlapping meanings. I would add that wisdom is the queen of all virtues because it encompasses other virtues such as humility and integrity, thoughtfulness and candor.

It is helpful to view expansions of these definitions from different perspectives. Some researchers in psychology have defined wisdom as the coordination of knowledge and experience and its deliberate use to improve well-being. They describe a wise person as follows:

- A wise person can discern the core of important problems.
- A wise person has self-knowledge [recalling Socrates' admonition to "know thyself"].
- A wise person seems sincere and direct with others [candor].
- Others ask wise people for advice.
- A wise person's actions are consistent with his/her ethical beliefs.

Although these definitions are helpful and wisdom is something all of us may recognize in a colleague, detecting it in advance, in a candidate, for example, is much more difficult. So we often rely on a few measures that can help. We can look for experience, especially the "hard-won, often bitter experience" described by Halberstam and as intuited by Sam Rayburn. By all accounts, running for sheriff in Texas and many other states is often such an experience.

This may be a bit easier if one considers some of the individual features of wisdom as described above, such as humility, candor, and signs of common sense and good judgment. Also, speaking by phone to current and prior colleagues of a faculty candidate (forget letters of recommendation for this purpose) has proved a crucial factor in my recruiting. This is especially effective if one knows the person from whom an assessment is sought. I often ask co-workers if they know anyone well at the candidate's institution and have them make the call.

The specific details of how one get's this information, particularly critical when assessing someone who will have leadership authority, are less important than keeping wisdom firmly in mind throughout the process. Errors in recruiting are more often made by indifference to this key measure than by using the wrong technique; ignoring signs of poor judgment or common sense also happens more often than it should.

Finally, I suspect that Rich's article was virtually finished when he learned that Barack Obama had added Paul Volcker, a seasoned veteran with "hard-won, often bitter experience," to his economic team; Rich acknowledged the wisdom of this choice at the very end of the article.

MAXIMS FOR CHANGING JOBS

> **One should consider an academic move only for an improvement in anticipated opportunity and environment of 50% or more.**

That cushion is needed because the true environment and opportunity almost always end up being less, and the difficulties always turn out to be more than one thought. It is in the nature of changes that the grass always looks greener, and it may be, but just not as green as it looked.

> **Every job relocation is due to a combina-tion of "push and pull"; however, the more "push" dominates the decision, the more unlikely the move will be satisfactory.**

The reason for this is obvious—one may be blinded to the warts on the new job by unhappiness in the old. For one in an unhappy job, it may be far better to suck it up and take more time to find a position with a stronger "pull." This maxim is difficult to observe when there is extreme unhappiness in a position—the temptation is to just get out, but it can be very risky.

> ## The job is what it is.

One must look primarily at the cake instead of the frosting, which can easily be manipulated to sell the job. Try to be realistic as to what the job is and is not. Review what authority and latitude your predecessor actually exercised and don't be fooled by vague promises that you can do more. A corollary of this maxim follows.

> **An organization in bad shape due to neglect and/or mismanagement will probably descend further for a time even after appropriate corrective action is begun.**

In other words, if you go into such a situation because of the opportunity it provides, don't expect sunny skies very soon. Things are likely to get worse, but as long as the direction seems right and the leadership and support are strong, the storm should pass. The reward for riding out the storm often is a strong sense of satisfaction and a bonding with fellow employees and colleagues that comes only from weathering a storm together. The bond can have lasting positive effects on the organization and its productivity.

> **If you are hired to solve an acute problem, you may no longer have leverage to build or expand the program once it is solved.**

Twice in my career I was given a new title, created for me, because there was a desperate need to solve a major acute problem. However, once I solved the acute problems and tried to exercise the authority that I thought those titles carried, my bosses became frightened and even angry. So beware of newly created titles or positions used to attract you and try to assess how much pressure the boss is under to make a change through you. Riding in on a white horse with fanfare may be good for the ego, but once you get off the horse, the fanfare will stop and you may step in manure. So one should identify the major problems and calculate what leverage is left once they are solved or defused. Get well-defined commitments to further development, not just vague promises. Carefully judge the character of your future boss and the likelihood that he/she will honor promises for future efforts once the main problems are solved. Discreetly asking those in the organization or others who know it well is the best way to get such information.

> **Be careful not to put too much weight on things that do not bear directly on your chances of succeeding in the job.**

Job satisfaction and accomplishment are the principal drivers of happiness for you and your family. That is far and away more important than a geographically idyllic location, institutional prestige, entitlements and social issues. If the job isn't working, none of the rest will matter much.

> **The "fit" in a new job often is not apparent for at least 18 months.**

This is true because assessing the "fit" will depend on the opportunity actually delivered by the institution and the energy focused on it by the individual, both of which take some time to assess. Many new recruits spend part of the first year wondering what possessed them to leave "home" or take that particular job in the first place; this is a normal reaction to the bite of reality.

Jobs are like oysters: if you can get past the rough shell, difficult opening and the booger-like inside, there is a tasty morsel and sometimes a pearl inside.

Religion, politics and all worthwhile human endeavors are the same; the pearl doesn't simply drop in your lap. You must find the oyster and work hard to dig it out of such an unlikely creature. And if there is food, but never a pearl, you may want to look elsewhere.

> **The time-course of academic jobs is like the classic sigmoid growth curve of bacteria in culture, with a lag phase, log growth phase and plateau.**

Continued healthy growth requires added nutrients (resources, opportunity), mutation (new scientific track or discovery) or re-plating into new medium (new job). None of these actions necessarily requires leaving one's institution, although that may be necessary. The trick is to be objective enough to know when one's career is approaching the plateau so a deliberate approach to the problem may begin. With no change in the culture medium, the plateau phase eventually is followed by bacterial (and academic) stagnation and or death.

> **Longevity in a position or institution is not a good measure of success, accomplishment or happiness.**

It is often a sign of inertia or excessive self-satisfaction. The infamous "gold watch" or its academic surrogates—a testimonial dinner, a plaque, or emeritus status—often turn out to be empty substitutes for engagement in more productive and satisfying activity, even if it is a risky change and requires leaving a familiar environment. Depending on the point in one's career, it may be better to do something quite different. It is a cliché, but true nonetheless, that we often fully realize too late that we go around in this life only once. As F. Scott Fitzgerald said, "There are no second acts in life," so we have just one complex first act in which we must improvise before the final curtain.

> **Academic battles are recurring and continuous and no one can win them all.**

It is best to enter a battle with overwhelming superiority in arms and ammunition, but for a *uniquely* important issue, one must be willing to put the job on the line, not as an idle threat or bluff, but in one's heart. If you would never leave and they know it, they have you by the gonads. Employees, and faculty are employees, have only one trump card after all is said and done—resignation with dignity on one's own terms. Of course, there are colleagues who are "lookers," who have never failed to look at a job when asked, often solely to gain leverage at the home institution. These sorts cry wolf too often causing disruption or uncertainty, and soon people begin to wish they would just go.

COMMENTARIES ON JOB CHANGES

Physicians as Job Negotiators

Recently I gave a seminar via the Internet (webinar) entitled, "Fundamentals of Negotiating-Tips for Fellows to Mid-Career Faculty." Some members of the American Society of Pediatric Hematology-Oncology had felt unprepared for negotiating the terms of a new job or for an improved arrangement or pay in an existing job. The topic of negotiation is an important one for physicians at all levels. How to do it, and what to negotiate, are key discussion and teaching points. I was asked by the ASPHO Professional Development Committee to address this issue. About 80 ASPHO members signed up to "attend."

Most of my talk was based on several simple principles of preparation (preparation! preparation!), approach and technique. I will summarize the talk and add some material that came from the submitted questions. I will later address the significant interest from applicants in how to negotiate improvement in their current jobs.

First, I will cover the nuts and bolts of being invited to look at a new job. I do this to provide a framework and timeline for the steps in the process I will later recommend.

A common sequence (it is not this way in all cases) starts

by receiving an invitation to visit an institution to consider a job opening there. Sometimes considering the job is implied rather than explicit and is couched in an invitation to give a seminar. In either case, it is common to be asked to make a relevant presentation. This first visit is an opportunity to meet as many people in your own specialty that would be colleagues if you went there. It is very important to obtain their contact information so you may ask questions or clarify issues after you leave. You may be asked if you would consider a move, and it is OK to say you are not sure or "yes, if the job turns out to be a good opportunity." However, do not commit to anything. This visit is a "freebie;" you incur no obligation to take the job or even explore it further.

If you are invited for a second visit, this should be taken seriously and only accept the invitation if there is a real possibility of a move. So get a sense from your spouse if there are any serious negative feelings about it before you accept the invitation. On this visit (or the next), your spouse is often invited as well; typically, you look at housing and schools, and you may receive an informal offer orally. Negotiating may begin informally, but be prepared and do not commit to anything at this point. You must have a detailed written offer to consider the job seriously.

Once you agree to the visit, you must start doing your homework in earnest beforehand. You must prepare to give a coherent vision of your short and long term goals and describe what value you bring to the institution. It will be important to practice describing this vision, preferably with a colleague in your present institution. You also must gather as much information as possible about the recruiting program (in this case, hematology-oncology). Is it a high quality program with a good reputation and a respectable grant and publication record? Are the clinical and support facilities ample (labs also, if relevant to you)? Is the clinical effort well organized and well staffed? Is the volume sufficient for clinical research? Are the clinical loads of future peers reasonable? Is there a good nurse practitioner program?

Sources for information include your current boss or other senior faculty (keep in mind that if they want to keep you they may try to dissuade you in their own interests, not yours). Fellows and faculty in the offering institution are good sources, as well as websites of the department or division and web searches of individuals there to judge productivity and tone of the program.

Get salary ranges, if possible, in your current institution and potential future institution. This is not always easy, so you may also go to the Association of American Medical Colleges, or, in this case, ASPHO; both periodically publish salary ranges for the various ranks. But keep in mind that these are not binding and some are often lower than reality because they do not include clinical or other incentives or bonuses.

You must also investigate what the financial needs of your family are. What is the cost of living in the new city compared to your current one? Do you have special financial needs, e.g. a chronically ill or handicapped child, loan repayments? What is the cost of housing, insurance, commuting to work and schools in the new environment? All of these and more will influence your family's financial needs.

Have a good idea of what you will need to earn for your family to be comfortable and why you need that much (loans, chronic illness, etc.). Have a deal breaker salary in mind, i.e. so low you cannot accept the job. Have a deal maker salary in mind, i.e. meets or exceeds your calculated needs.

Some of this research will be undertaken on the second (or later) visit. You should have detailed discussions with persons in the program face to face or by phone (not by email, in which they may be less candid). Have promises been kept concerning workload and academic time? Has the environment been productive for those at your level? How is your future boss to work for? Is he or she always on the road? Try to have as much actual data as possible, which puts you in a stronger negotiating position.

If you plan to carry out laboratory research, be prepared. Don't underestimate the time you need for your lab work to be grant-competitive. Starting out with a few months to work 100% in the lab would help you get a good start. Do not break up your day, e.g. half day in the lab and another half in the clinic, but have days set aside for one or the other. In a split day, both will suffer. Be certain there are lab scientists there that work in your general scientific area; if you are a junior faculty member try to identify and hook up with a lab mentor; without either, failure is more likely.

You now have a written offer in hand. Study the specifics and see if anything is missing. Are your duties and responsibilities and the time required to carry them out well clearly defined? Are salary and benefits clearly described? Is the offer for tenure track, clinical track or a contract arrangement? What are the requirements for promotion?

There likely will be subsequent negotiation, which may occur face to face or electronically. If they give indications that they want you, soak it in, take notes and ask for clarifications if needed. Ask questions but give few opinions at this point ("I will need to think about that") unless you are rock solid sure of something. If you have done your homework and have data, you should feel confident that you know the landscape and possibilities, and know what the deal breakers are for you.

Be confident but not cocky. Don't be afraid to say, "I don't know" or "I don't understand" or "That might be a problem." Never say, "It's up to my spouse." This is a very off-putting excuse. If you and/or your spouse do not want to go there for any reason at any point in the discussions, your response should be, "It is just not a good fit for me/us at this time" or "We have come to realize that we are very happy where we are."

Now they want you and you want the job so the final negotiation begins. Notify them that you want the job but need changes or clarification in the written offer...salary, workload, duties, lab setup, etc. Many terms are negotiable but some are not because they are hard-wired in the institutional regulations, e.g. insurance or promotions policy. They may say I can give you A and B, but not C or D. Only you can decide how important C or D is to you compared to how badly you want the job.

Keep in mind that you are in the strongest position to bargain before you sign the acceptance. Once you sign, it is over, so push for what you must have. For something critically important and vital to your success, don't count on a response of "maybe next year when finances are better." Most important, you must have confidence in your new boss and institution to treat you well and fairly and help you along. If that confidence is lacking, do not take the job and move on (gut feelings are important barometers).

What about those who do not want to move but want to better their situation? This was a common question and almost always revolved around an "inadequate salary." In some programs, the leader has an annual "career assessment" meeting with faculty. If so, what I will say can be done at that meeting. If not in your case, I suggest you request such a meeting AFTER you have done all the preparation and research that I have noted above.

You state that you want to meet to ask for advice on your career development. You are concerned that you are not growing professionally and this is reflected in your inadequate salary. What can you do to improve both? This is a hard thing for many people to do. You fear angering the boss and being worse off. But if he declines to change anything, you must push for an explanation. If you absolutely do not want to move, you may have trapped yourself. If that is the case, I suggest that you still look at other jobs (one visit only) to get a sense of your value to others and to see what the landscape is out there. Preferably, this should be done before you have your meeting as part of your preparation, but it could be done after. You cannot sit tight and wish something good happens. If things are very bad and you cannot find, your only options are to move to another faculty position or change your career path (Pharma, health care administration, etc.).

Traps to avoid: 1) They really only want you to carry a large clinical load—clues include amount of on-service and clinic time and grousing faculty about no academic time (some always grouse so this is a valid clue only if widespread). 2) You and/ or your spouse love the geographic location (San Diego, hometown, etc.) so much that you don't question the key professional issues or push hard for what you must have to succeed and live comfortably. 3) The institution's stature is impressive so, once again you do not adequately question the key professional issues critical to your personal development.

Seismic Changes in Medical Practice

My work with ASCO's Quality Oncology Practice Initiative since 2002 had unexpected positive side effects. The friendships and professional relationships made with community oncologists, particularly those who represented the 23 founding practices that built and tested QOPI, have been personally rewarding in many ways.

The most surprising result of these relationships has been the progressive growth of my insight and understanding of a world I never worked in—the private practice of oncology. While there is no substitute for practice itself for gaining a full understanding of the rewards and challenges, working with these oncologists has taught me a lot. The more I learned the more interested I became in the issues facing community oncology practices.

Surprisingly, oncologists in academia face many of the same issues. In fact, all physicians, practices and hospitals are trying to deal with a maelstrom of conditions with unpredictable effects, such as declining reimbursement, accountable care organizations (ACOs), the Affordable Care Act (ACA), the changing attitudes of newer physicians and the still shaky financial environment here at home and abroad. These factors have already led providers to make voluntary professional changes that seem to be accelerating.

The most dramatic of these changes is the river of physicians giving up independent practice to become employed by hospitals, large non-profit organizations such as the Permanente Medical Groups, the Geisinger Clinic and others. Also, experienced community oncologists are being recruited to manage academic medical clinics using their in-the-trenches experience.

The formation of ACOs, essentially collaborative provider groups that are reimbursed as a unit, is part of the ACA. This has led to a scramble by hospitals and health systems to employ physicians so that costs of the entire episode of care may be controlled with the expectation that profit margins would increase. The need to control medical costs is a major rationale for the ACA, of course.

Some hospitals and health systems have gone even further on this track. They are reorganizing their administrative structures to include doctors in leadership roles, a canny move since controlling costs will require physician trust and collaboration. As reported by John Iglehart in the April 2001 issue of Health Affairs, the huge for-profit health system HCA is reorganizing to form ACOs and to increase their employed physician roster substantially above the current 2,000.

Perhaps the most intriguing example offered by Iglehart is the announcement in March 2011 by Carilion Clinic, the largest health care provider in southwest Virginia that it was joining forces with the insurer Aetna to form an ACO and offer cobranded commercial health plans for businesses and individuals. In 2006 Carilion seemingly anticipated the shifts in health care by changing from a hospital organization to become a physician-led clinic "bent on offering more patient-centered, coordinated care at lower cost. As a consequence, Carilion, which already employed a number of primary care doctors, added approximately 200 specialists in fields such as cardiology and radiology, and now it has an employed-physician base of roughly 600."

But other factors are also playing a role in these seismic changes.

Reimbursement declines since passage of the 2003 Medicare Modernization Act, which increased pharmaceutical benefits for seniors using funds previously paid to doctors for medications and their administration, have taken a heavy toll on smaller primary care and specialty practices. This led to many oncologists in particular joining larger practices and other multispecialty oncology groups., both for-profit, e.g. US Oncology and non-profit, e.g. the Permanente Medical Groups.

Many physicians are tired of trying to maintain an independent business with the reimbursement woes, increasing regulation and liability costs, and the inability to afford the purchase and maintenance of an electronic health record system. So they are "seeking shelter from the storms of private practice in the arms of larger and better financed hospitals." Iglehart also reports that in the past year about half of all cardiologists in private practice have become employed, mostly by hospitals. Jack Lewin, CEO of the American College of Cardiology, says the trend is driven almost entirely by "Medicare's drastic cuts in payments for services in outpatient offices [the] same services for which Medicare pays two to three times as much in hospital outpatient settings."

Another factor propelling this seismic shift is that younger physicians and many women physicians are willing to forego greater income in exchange for the increased family time possible as an employed physician. Many also see owning and running a practice as stressful and unattractive, especially in the current climate of financial and professional uncertainty.

A survey by the Medical Group Management Association shows that in 2002, physicians owned 70% of practices and hospitals owned 25%. In 2009 physicians owned 40% of practices and hospitals owned 55%. That trend has not leveled off as yet.

The $64 question (that amount shows how old I am): Is this trend good for oncology patients and/or oncologists? Well, possibly. There are substantial hurdles to making these changes lead to higher quality care at lower cost.

First, doctors and hospitals have a long history to tense and unproductive relationships when that outcome depends on strong collaboration and mutual sacrifice. Older physicians who have developed a certain way of practicing and a lifestyle built on the old model may ultimately find such arrangements constraining. Such complex, long-term relationships require strong leadership by physicians and hospital administrators that can be threatened by the turnover of key leaders.

However, we know that it is possible for this integrated model to succeed from many long-standing examples such as the Mayo Clinic and Kaiser Permanente. Also, some hospitals have changed their management structures to include physicians at the highest levels of administration, including seats on the board of directors.

Second, arguments over money can sow distrust and anger, leading to festering wound in the relationships. Earning trust would require a high degree of transparency and joint planning and agreement on the terms of such rewards. Hospitals would be able to reward physician employees for productivity while they could not do so for volunteer physicians because of Stark regulations. Also, under the reform bill and ACOs, Medicare is breaking with past restrictions by encouraging physician alliances, banding doctors together to cut costs and share in savings with insurers.

Finally, if implemented, will ACOs do what is intended, i.e. improve the quality of care and lower costs? My most optimistic answer is probably. Certainly, it will not work uniformly well and will fail at some sites. The tests so far have shown that it takes years to demonstrate savings, if they occur at all. Ironically, I think it may be easier to lower or stabilize costs than to demonstrate a substantial improvement in quality. The latter can happen, of course, but measuring quality is an evolving science and, except for a few areas of narrowly focused processes, e.g. reducing catheter-caused infections, acceptable, apples-to-apples outcome standards for complex diseases like cancer are not in place. Fortunately, work in this area is proceeding apace.

So I believe it is more likely than not that patients will to be better off in the long run and costs will be stabilized (that is as certain as I can be at this stage). Will oncologists be better off? With at least some success, in the long haul I believe the answer is Yes for a couple of reasons. If the patients are better off, we as physicians are "better off" because we have been successful in our core mission. Second, all agree that the current system is not sustainable and, if not addressed quickly, draconian cuts in services that hurt patients will be forced on us. So participating in an attempt to head that off and helping to shape it to protect patients has become a part of our mission. Who better to do that than those of us serving patients?

In his wonderful commencement address at Harvard Medical School (*New Yorker,* 26 May 2011) Atul Gawande eloquently made this case. He likened the cowboy, the iconic loner, to the fiercely independent physician we have known up to now. He then compared cowboys, a collection of loners, to pit crews at the auto racetrack, who are the epitome of intense collaboration, efficiency and teamwork.

He said, in effect, we are in a new era of medical complexity, sub-specialization and growing problems of patient access and cost. He believes we must be more like pit crews in today's world to achieve the greatest good for the most people. He ends by saying he recently spoke to a real cowboy who described the nature of his work in 2011; it has evolved to become much like the pit crews, with careful planning and electronic communication to move and handle cattle. I would like to think that if cowboys can do it with cattle and pit crews can do it with cars, we could do it for our patients.

Professional Migrations of Oncologists

This is a follow up of the essay above that appeared in an earlier issue of *Oncology Times,* "Seismic Changes in Medical Practice," I described the large professional movement of physicians, including subspecialists; many of these are from ownership of a private practice to employment. This migration has been attributed to poor reimbursement, health care reform, over regulation of practices, the hassle of bookkeeping and insurance, a desire for more family time, and mental fatigue.

In order to drill down on specific factors faced by oncologists, I have interviewed four medical oncologists who have made the switch to uncover the reasons, process and outcomes of the professional moves. I know each of them personally and have worked with them on projects for ASCO. I interviewed them mainly by email.

1. Dr. Douglas Blayney was in a private medical oncology group with many practice sites in suburban Los Angeles for 17 years before taking the Medical Director position at the University of Michigan Cancer Center. He recently served as president of ASCO and this year moved back to California to a similar position at Stanford.

What are the main reasons that led you to make the change?
D.B.- Professionally it was time to make a change. I was tired of the commute and the traffic. In the managed care system that developed in Los Angeles, I found myself in more and more uncomfortable situations regarding treatment decisions. Most importantly, the opportunity at the University of Michigan was a great time to leverage my experience and interests while continuing to practice clinical oncology (which I love); there were more opportunities for formal guidance and mentoring at the U of M. There are great people in both places, whom I enjoyed very much.

I found the thoughts of Peter Drucker, the management theorist, [useful. He] writes about knowledge workers (such as physicians) who max out their skills in their mid- fifties and have twenty more years to work. With knowledge workers, as opposed to manual workers who were often worn out by their fifties, a second career which combines doing well the job of the first career (which by then comes easily) and acquiring new skills, is very common. I have recommended Drucker's writings to friends and colleagues contemplating a second career.

How did the opportunity arise...ad, word of mouth, or recommendation?
D.B.- I was contacted by a recruiter, who knew of my work within ASCO. I did not look at any other jobs at that time.

How did you finally decide to move and why that particular job?
D.B.- It seemed like a good idea at the time. Our children were at points in their education (two in college, one about to start middle school) when family disruption was minimal, and my wife had accomplished all she could in her teaching job.

Was the move a good one professionally and personally?
D.B.-Yes. We were able to move from California to the Midwest, a region of the country where we had never lived, and from a suburban to a rural environment. We made some great friends, both personal and professional. I was able to obtain training and develop skills by working with a broad range of hospital professionals and easily take courses in the Business School which would have been much more difficult in my practice setting.

What are the main reasons it has been a good move? Any regrets?
D.B.- I have learned new skills, made contributions in areas I

couldn't have in my previous settings, and looked forward to going to work every day.

Do you think there are such opportunities out there for oncologists who might like to consider such a move?
D.B.- Yes. I get calls or inquiries about twice per month. Peter Drucker, when he writes about knowledge workers and second careers, cautions that one needs to acquire the skills for the second career during the first. He uses the example of becoming a professional musician or chef as a career switch -- the skills for the new career should be gradually acquired during the first career, otherwise the second career will be a disaster.

2. Dr. Dean Gesme was in private oncology practice for 24 years in Cedar Rapids, Iowa, before moving to a US Oncology practice in Minnesota.

What are the main reasons that led you to make the change?
D.G.- I was becoming complacent and bored, I needed a new challenge as affirmed by my wife who encouraged my wanderlust. My kids were grown and gone and our grandkids (and kids) were in Minneapolis and San Diego, making these the destinations of choice for myself and my wife—as you well understand. I was involved in several start-up oncology businesses (patient education website, oncology business news, patient financial assistance, cancer rehab) and I wanted a part-time clinical position that would allow for these ventures (two went bust in the capital market meltdown but others are doing well). Another reason for change was that I needed a better airport as I was flying a lot as a consultant, investor in new busi-

nesses, volunteer, and visiting grandkids. Cedar Rapids had few direct connections, while Minneapolis allowed national and international connections to most desired destinations.

How did the opportunity arise...ad, word of mouth, or recommendation?
D.G.- I made the opportunity. The practice I joined was not recruiting but they were open to my part-time employment as I had helped them when they first came together and joined US Oncology. I also knew several doctors from the University of Minnesota where I had been before practice in Iowa. I had looked at [academic] Clinical Director positions on the West Coast and at the University of Michigan. I had accepted at Michigan but they pulled the rug out after the fact on my clinical appointment and, on the advice of a mentor (dean of a med school who always called it straight) and my wife, I waved goodbye to academia and contacted Doug Blayney who applied after me and hopefully used some of my disappointments in shaping his position at UM.

Has this been a good move? Any regrets?
D.G.- No real regrets. Although academia was a very tempting alternative, [there may have been] too many restrictions and expectations for my satisfaction. The move has been great for me from the standpoint of refreshing my clinical skills and bringing me into areas of oncology that I hadn't thought possible in Cedar Rapids, e.g. multidisciplinary team building for premier head and neck and esophageal cancer programs. I also continue to pursue new business ventures in oncology and enjoy working with the young people in those businesses and with teaching medical residents.

Do you think there are such opportunities out there for oncologists who might like to consider such a move?

D.G.- I see many oncologists who [know] how short life can be but also seem frozen into styles of life and habits of practice that prevent them from dreaming of how things might be different or better! Our comfort zone after years of training and high achievement seems to be very narrow—little imagination takes place as we confine ourselves to what others define as successful lifestyles. Almost every oncologist has far more options than they have ever considered. Who else can make as much money, enjoy cutting edge science, participate in major ways in our patient's lives, and make their own lifestyle than can an oncologist? It is not restricted opportunity but rather restricted comfort zones that make or break our opportunities, in my opinion.

3. Dr. Michael Neuss was in a private practice in Cincinnati for 25 years until a very recent move to Vanderbilt.

What are the main reasons that led you to make the change?

M.N.- The pull was the opportunity to see life from the other side and be on the cutting edge as we move into an era of personalized, genetics-based treatments and set up multidisciplinary care with new payment and quality metrics models and the opportunity to try life in a new city. The push was the [progressively] increasing emphasis on the finances of private practice.

How did the opportunity arise...ad, word of mouth, recommendation?

M.N.- I was recommended by a colleague.

Did you look at other jobs at that time?
M.N.- Yes, three others—one hospital based non-academic and two other academic jobs which were/are very similar to this one.

How did you finally decide to move and why that particular job?
M.N.- You are the Sicilian, but they made me an offer I couldn't refuse, with a very reasonable reporting structure, great support and clear goals that should be doable. A key factor was that my wife, Gwyneth, said it would be fun, and that she was willing to give up one of the best jobs of her career as a school nurse for special needs children, to support the adventure.

Was the move a good one professionally and personally (so far)?
M.N.- Professionally, it's very difficult to leave longstanding patients who have given their trust at one of the worst moments in their lives. It feels like I'm abandoning them, and for a variety of reasons, I did make a clean break and that makes it worse. However, there are patients here too and there is some relief to go "off service." Personally, the kids are grown, the dog was dead, and the disruption, while very real, is also very exciting and fun. So personally, great so far. And professionally, I'm working on it.

What are the main reasons it has been a good or a bad move? Any regrets (so far)?
M.N.- The best part, which is more important than I realized it

would be, is the opportunity to be around young people. The opportunity to be challenged clinically or otherwise by really smart and enthusiastic people is phenomenally satisfying. The fun of being unsettled and in a new environment is generally great.

Do you think there are such opportunities out there for oncologists who might like to consider such a move?
M.N.- There seem to be but it's hard to be concrete. I hear stories, but not details

4. Dr. Joseph Jacobson was in a hospital-owned community practice in Peabody, Massachusetts for 14 years, 7 years in full time oncology practice and 7 years in part time practice plus medical administration. He accepted a position at the Dana-Farber Cancer Institute earlier this year.

How long were you in your prior practice and where was it located?
J.J.- I was never in private practice but in a hospital-owned community practice full-time for 7 years, then part-time for another 7. The practice is located in Peabody Massachusetts.

What are the main reasons that led you to make the change?
J.J.- I was mostly employed as a Chair of Medicine (80%) for the last 7 years and was beginning to drift away from oncology. My practice for the last two years had been limited to the inpatient setting. The opportunity that I was given allowed me to return to focus full-time in cancer and for the first time in my career, to be paid to work on quality improvement.

How did the opportunity arise...ad, word of mouth, recommendation?
J.J.- I was recruited. It was unsolicited. I wasn't looking or even thinking of moving.

Did you look at other jobs at that time?
J.J.- No.

How did you finally decide to move and why that particular job?
J.J.-The opportunity to play a major role in helping shape the care at DFCI was compelling.

Was the move a good one professionally and personally?
J.J.- SFSG (so far so good).

What are the main reasons it has been a good or a bad move? Any regrets (so far)?
J.J.- I have moved into an intellectually stimulating environment full of challenges and unknowns....a huge gift at this juncture in my career.

Do you think there are such opportunities out there for oncologists who might like to consider such a move?
J.J.- I suspect that more and more oncologists will become employed, and that there will be leadership opportunities of various types that will become available.

So there you have four different stories of senior medical oncologists taking a chance at doing something more exciting and stimulating. Change is risky, they tell us, but it also can rejuvenate one's career, open new doors, teach one a lot, and challenge one's capacities for change and adaptation that brings out the best in us.

Are these changes a unique sign of the times? No, many physicians have always changed their professional duties in mid-career, sometimes for advancement, but just as often for the reasons given above—boredom (first on my personal list), unhappiness with medical trends, and fear of losing skills because one works daily among those with the same ideas. Others have made more dramatic changes in careers, becoming poets, writers, politicians or businessmen and women in industry.

When my daughter told me she wanted to go to medical school, I was thrilled, not because I wanted to brag about my daughter the doctor (which I do anyway), but because of the broad array of professional opportunities the profession and its spinoffs offer. For a female physician 25 years ago, this was an especially important consideration and the relative financial security the profession offers makes such career changes more possible.

We physicians are blessed with multiple opportunities. But, as Doug Blayney said about the advice of Peter Drucker, one must prepare for the potential change years ahead by using some skills one has acquired (Consulting? Take serious cooking lessons?). I needn't remind you that life is short and that we go around only once. If one looks at opportunities when they come along but decides against a move, that is also a good thing because it may reinforce your satisfaction with your current role. But if an exciting chance comes along at the right time... take it!

Professional Careers for Old Guys

As I write this column it is exactly three weeks from my turning over the reins of a cancer center to the new director. That was one of my several goals when I took this job 17 months ago and I am delighted that we have recruited an excellent successor. So it is time for assessing this adventure, particularly from the viewpoint of what older guys in medicine, particularly academic medicine, may do late in their careers.

But first some background. My career since I reached eligibility for Medicare has largely consisted of doing sequential, short-term projects, such as consulting of various types. My earlier career was typical, holding a specific position in an institution that had implicit goals, but also was an open-ended responsibility for all or part of an organization. At first I didn't understand the full meaning of this transition; upon reflection I found that it suited me at this time in my career. Although it seemed risky to give up a well-paying job that I could have continued indefinitely, I took the plunge, despite the fact that many colleagues questioned my sanity.

My thinking went something like this. I was no longer in the career-building mode; I had no desire to write more papers or submit another grant. So the risk was more financial than professional and that risk was small since my TIAA-CREF pension fund had become adequate to sustain my wife and me. In effect, any additional income would be frosting on the cake since our children were grown and financially independent and we lived modestly with no mortgage and no debts. Both of us were born in the middle of the Great Depression and the hard-won lessons were passed on to us by our parents. This gave us enormous freedom to choose to do what we wished without the traditional financial burdens.

In more practical terms, the daily life I shifted into was idyllic in many ways: I worked from home with a 25-foot commute to my office; I lunched every day with my wife; I had no employees and no boss; I was free to accept or reject job opportunities based on how interesting they might be rather than the revenue they might generate. My motive for working was to stay intellectually engaged, to continue learning, and to have the freedom to engage in other projects of interest, like service on the National Cancer Policy Board at the Institute of Medicine and starting the Quality Oncology Practice Initiative at ASCO. The only downside was that I served as my own IT director; talk about steep learning curves!

I agreed to become a temporary cancer center director as a direct result of consulting jobs I had done, but mainly I was quite interested in the proposed consortium arrangement between two academic institutions. These relationships are very difficult to pull off and I wanted to understand all the barriers and potential advantages first hand. The job was time-limited with specific goals achievable in the short time frame, an essential requirement for me. Other factors in the equation were that it would require a domestic move (bad) that would put us a relatively short drive from our two pre-school grandsons (very, very good!).

So what have I learned about jobs for old guys, including me? First, many of my colleagues are quite content to continue their academic careers in situ, perhaps shifting more to teaching, patient care, administrative chores, or even staying active in grant-supported research. They continue to enjoy the academic life with its ebb and flow of committee service, students and trainees and the like. Good for them; they can provide a valuable service and there is security in those positions. The risk, of course is stagnation and boredom, two factors that I personally fear much more than insecurity.

Second, non-permanent long-term jobs, one year or more, are hard. If one commutes, that is a lot of travel and hotel occupancy. If one is contemplating a household move, one must consider the financial issues, housing markets, the unpleasantness and angst inherent in all moves, and whether one might possibly stay in the area when the job was finished. In my case, easy access to grandchildren was a major factor. For a previous job, which required almost constant presence on site, I rented an apartment paid for by the client. But all of these long jobs are hard work so the likely upside in job satisfaction and learning something new must be substantial.

The third lesson (re-learned) was the recurring, almost daily frustration one faces in large academic organizations, especially in universities with medical schools and hospitals. Though the specifics vary from place to place, it never abates very much. In my career I found less frustration in freestanding cancer centers, but not dramatically less. The factors that increase or decrease frustrations most depend on organizational culture ("we always do it this way"), the personalities of the hierarchy (micromanager, south end o f the horse, etc), the institution's scientific and clinical standards (tolerance of shoddy workmanship), and the decisiveness and strength of the leadership ("we know what to do but can't get a decision from above").

Finally, despite the negatives, this late career professional course has been good for me. I have learned a lot, met some great people I would not have otherwise, and have some modest accomplishments to point to. Now that this job will soon end, I have the opportunity to try something new and different. I have no specific plans...but it is not necessary to have any plans at this stage of my career. Something interesting always pops up. I don't know how or why that happens, but it does. And if it didn't, taking a break and visiting more with my grandsons isn't a bad alternative.

In my view, you only go around once in this world, so carpe diem, seize the day, take some career risks and make the best of it; love your family and have some fun.

Change: The Good, the Bad and the Ugly

My wife and I have just moved (again); I hope it is the last before my trip to the nursing home. Moving is a pain, as most of you know all too well. It is a more dramatic and stressful change than the day-to-day changes which most of us hardly notice. You know all the clichés: change is inevitable; change is good; change for the sake of change is a bad idea. But this latest moving experience, more stressful than most of ours because of the bad housing market, has given me time to think about the wide spectrum of change experiences and their complexities.

In April I wrote about change in organizations. In this column, with a nod to Clint Eastwood and the famous "spaghetti western," I focus on personal change, how it affects us and how we cope...or not.

In many ways, relocation of a household has many features in common with changes in careers, personal relationships, economic status, health and other human experiences. Oftentimes, two or more distinct changes occur simultaneously, such as, moving to a new job in a different city. The process has some features, though not nearly as severe or lasting, of the death of a loved one or a divorce. I address mainly changes of job, profession, household, and relationships.

Relief (Phase 1) is often the first emotion. A period of indecision can be protracted while one gathers information for considering a new job, a household move, and new responsibilities. These major decisions have a broad effect on others, such as family members, colleagues and even institutions, which must be considered. Once a decision has been made there is a period of relief that the stress of deciding is over; a decision for change has been made. This period of relief is brief, however, because a new emotion takes its place.

Anxiety (Phase 1) replaces relief for many reasons. There are always questions about the wisdom of the choice that tend to recur for an extended period of time ("I had a nice job, why did I bring this on myself?"). The full impact of the move on family, friends and colleagues now become more apparent and seemingly irreversible. And as the anxiety declines or stabilizes regarding one issue, a new overlapping anxiety pops up. For example, the anxiety about whether the new job was a wise choice is soon overcome by the search for a new place to live and selling the current home. The latter has become a suffocating anxiety in the current housing market. Many of my colleagues have had to move before selling their home leaving them with two mortgages and worry without end. This sometimes moves to an even more difficult emotional stage.

"Fear and trembling" (with a nod to St. Paul and the Danish philosopher, Soren Kierkegaard) is often the next stage. The cumulative stress grows as the house fails to sell; the homes to purchase are too expensive for one's budget unless the current house sells; your teenage kids are angry and talk about wanting to stay put to finish high school; the new boss and new colleagues are on the phone to you about matters to decide or problems to consider before you are even there; you find your devoted and supportive spouse crying or mumbling about "nothing." You start wondering if you will screw up your family or get into a tough financial hole or hate the new job. Sleepless nights are common. Then the moving day is set.

Anxiety (Phase 2) is a complex mixture of confusion, stress and deadlines. My change of address notifications went to 40 distinct entities not counting family, friends and colleagues: bank, social security, utilities, professional societies, phone and credit card companies, etc. The moving process itself, packing, trying to anticipate how things will fit in the new house, disruption of daily routines, and for surprisingly long periods being frozen with nothing to do because of timing or the inaccessibility of tools for doing something.

Relief (Phase 2) comes after the family is moved into the new home. Boxes are everywhere, but at least you are there and together and will have time to get settled. Everything is new so finding places to shop, schools and Starbucks is a recurring, sometimes frustrating and sometimes rewarding exercise. The children are texting old friends 24/7 but they are also slowly making new friends. The job is more challenging than you thought, but the new environment and colleagues invigorate you. But this period also ends when the practical aspects of the change take charge of your time and energy.

Acceptance, adaptation and hard work become the dominant factors in your day. We are here and have a thousand things to put away and to organize and we must establish new routines. And we must adapt. The latter can be very difficult in both the job and household. The job exists in an established culture that you are unlikely to change, so you must find a way to adapt while maintaining your productivity. The household must be rearranged to fit the new physical and neighborhood dimensions that are always different from the old ones.

Settling in is the usual last phase. The family adapts and makes new friends. The job is interesting and the challenges become opportunities. In short, a new home is created in a new environment.

Occasionally, things do not work out. There are two major reasons why this happens: mama isn't happy, and if mama isn't happy, no one is happy. This can be caused by fear and loneliness (leaving parents or siblings, husband is working 14 hours a day) or a general unease with the environment. The other main reason is that the job didn't work out: promised resources were not delivered or the guy who hired you left soon after and your new chief is the south end of a horse.

On the whole, however, when change is made for the right reasons, e.g. professional and family opportunity, things eventually work out, though it takes 18 months or more for that to be realized. In my personal experience, every career and household move has led to more positive than negative experiences, even my one "unsuccessful" move; the latter taught me much more per unit time about organizations and people than the "successful" moves.

Thus, with qualifications, the clichés are correct: change is good, when made with the right motives and expectations; change is inevitable, even if one does not leave one's home or institution—it is just less noticeable and can sneak up on you; change for the sake of change is a bad idea, and this is the ugliest form of change because it more often than not leads to unhappiness.

MAXIMS ON VALUES AND SUCCESS

This section differs from the others in two ways. First, it contains only three maxims; the rest is a collection of loosely related essays. These deal not only with success, but also with the satisfaction of doing good work and upholding important values such as civility and the nobility of work. It also deals with late career changes, opportunities and experiences, using myself, a certified "old guy," as an example. They also address the sometimes profound influence of chance on careers.

> **There are strong temptations to compromise one's academic mission by unhealthy alliances with sources of power or dollars.**

The potential dangers of entanglements with the for-profit industry are usually recognized, if often ignored or disdained. Few oncologists, for example, acknowledge that they are being influenced, manipulated and seduced by industry, especially the pharmaceutical and biotechnology industries. Payment for enrolling patients on studies, lavish parties and exhibits at professional meetings, well-compensated seats on boards of directors and other financial emoluments have a subtle or overt influence on professional behavior.

Is there a major academic medical center today that doesn't have substantial financial ties to for-profit companies? Academics with seats on the boards of for-profit companies, stock options or lucrative consulting contracts are commonplace. Many clinical trials are now generously supported by industry, providing an important source of revenue in academic medical centers. Sometime, somehow, somewhere, the piper will be paid.

> **Academic success, ironically, depends a great deal on recognizing and adapting to the dominant cultural and financial features of one's era.**

There are different ways to divide these eras. In my view, there are four overlapping eras relevant to this thesis; though dates of primacy are given, features of all persist today. The Oslerian Era (1900-45) was dominated by diagnostic skills, anatomic and clinical pathology and public health. Academic positions were few and poorly paid. Effective therapeutic tools were limited in number. The autopsy was the basis of the most important conference at academic medical centers. Full-time faculty were few in number and the "professor" of a department was usually the chairman and the best clinician—a superb diagnostician often asked to consult in difficult cases. The large charity hospitals like Cook County in Chicago, Bellevue in New York, Boston City and Charity in New Orleans were prime teaching centers staffed by elite academic faculty. Childhood immunizations, improved sanitation and general anesthesia had a profound impact on health. Much of the medical research was done either in pathology departments that had access to most of the clinical data, pre- and post-mortem, or in a few major research institutions on the East Coast such as the Thorndike Laboratories at Harvard, Johns Hopkins and the Rockefeller Institute. This was the era of the medical Renaissance man— superb clinician, investigator and teacher, often well read.

Next came the NIH Rapid Growth Era (1945-70) that saw the NIH become the premier, almost obligatory, training ground for academicians, as well as the financial engine for research medical centers all over the country. Faculty in academic medical centers grew exponentially with the NIH dollars that made up 70-90% the budget of many departments in premier research centers. This is when the NIH grantees became kings, often allowed to disdain clinical or teaching duties because they were an important source of prestige and dollars for the institution.

The Medicare-Medicaid Era (1965-90) saw academic centers restructure to increase the newly available clinical revenues that were generous enough to allow cost shifting to support research and teaching. This is when the high revenue specialists, such as surgeons, pathologists, interventional cardiologists and radiologists, became kings and shaped the agendas of many academic medical centers.

Academic medical centers are now in the For-Profit Era (1980-?). The dominant forces with the greatest impact on their missions, for good or ill, are managed care, health systems, and the pharmaceutical and biotechnology industry. While more and more investigators compete for grants, industrial research has increased and the surplus from clinical revenues has declined steeply. Thus, to sustain and develop programs, faculty and institutions have increasingly looked to industry for support. Is there a major academic medical center today that doesn't have substantial financial ties to for-profit companies? Academics with seats on the boards of for-profit companies, stock options or lucrative consulting contracts are commonplace. Many clinical trials are now generously supported by industry, providing an important source of revenue in academic medical centers.

By recognizing one's era, it is possible to know where the power lies. Whether one participates or not, one must recognize and find a way to adapt to the large forces in one's era. Failure to do so may lead to despair; this is one reason many older physicians are unhappy. However, there is a serious risk that one will undergo metamorphosis rather than adaptation-- forfeiting rather than sustaining one's professional values and commitment to public service.

There are strong temptations to compromise one's academic mission by unhealthy alliances with sources of power or dollars. The potential dangers of entanglements with the for-profit industry are usually recognized, if often ignored or disdained. Few oncologists, for example, acknowledge that they are being influenced, manipulated and seduced by industry, especially the pharmaceutical and biotechnology industries. Payment for enrolling patients on studies, lavish parties and exhibits at professional meetings, well-compensated seats on boards of directors and other financial emoluments have a subtle or overt influence on professional behavior.

Further, even fewer appreciate the potential dangers of government and philanthropic support. It is possible for a so-so scientist to become a well-funded, ace "grantsman," who follows the safe scientific niche rather than the riskier, but more interesting course. A tally of grant dollars may be over-weighted in judging the success and value of a faculty member. The peer review process can only take a snapshot through a microscope. The skills of grantsmanship are important and grant support is certainly a key measure of success, but obtaining grants is not a perfect surrogate for scientific skills and certainly cannot address the scientific or clinical yeast the person brings to a program. I have seen not a few CVs of well-funded investigators who have little of substance to show for it, with little solid work published in strong journals.

Philanthropy can be seductive and many of us look upon it as "free money." But there are many examples of philanthropists influencing operations adversely or supporting substandard faculty or programs, leading to poor scientific and academic decisions. The strings attached to philanthropic giving are often subtle or invisible; it isn't easy to say "no" to a rich and eager donor. With the best of intentions, philanthropists may cause one to build a facility before it is programmatically indicated or before operating revenue has been secured. Or they may cause a shift in scientific focus that is poorly grounded in opportunity. Skill and tact are necessary to align the needs and wishes of the donor with the long-term interests of the academic program.

Academic medicine is a noble calling. Despite the problems, it can be the most fulfilling and rewarding of professions, if taken with a sharp eye for reality, a dash of iconoclasm and a ready sense of humor. These jobs are difficult and certainly not rewarding 24 hours a day; sometimes we are lucky to get 24 hours a month. But we in academic medicine are blessed in many ways compared to those in most jobs. We have the privilege of working in a profession that helps the sick and dying while we are engaged in intellectual inquiry. Our profession is still highly respected by society and we are paid quite well for doing something most of us love to do. So despite all the travails of human frailty that we must deal with every day, we should count our blessings. I am grateful that fate and early training led me into academic medicine and would do it again in a New York minute.

> **All work done well has the character of nobility, regardless of the job.**

We can't all be CEOs of Fortune 500 companies, but anyone can take satisfaction in a job well done—giving one's full effort to the task at hand and enjoying the satisfaction that comes from it. When done this way, any job can have a degree of nobility. This should be so even in temporary or menial jobs, since one's work ethic is not easy to turn on and off.

In my own case, I have always felt that academic medicine was a noble calling. Despite the problems, it can be the most fulfilling and rewarding of professions, if taken with a sharp eye for reality, a dash of iconoclasm and a ready sense of humor. These jobs are difficult and certainly not rewarding 24 hours a day; sometimes we are lucky to get 24 hours a month.

But we in academic medicine are blessed in many ways compared to those in most jobs. We have the privilege of working in a profession that helps the sick and dying while we are engaged in intellectual inquiry. Our profession is still highly respected by society and we are paid quite well for doing something most of us love to do. So despite all the travails of human frailty that we must deal with every day, we should count our blessings. I am grateful that fate and early training led me into academic medicine and would do it again in a New York minute.

COMMENTARIES ON VALUES AND SUCCESS

"The Stonemason" on the Integrity and Sanctity of Work

I rarely read works of literature cover to cover a second time; the great majority I read through once and only portions thereafter. But a few I read cover to cover repeatedly, as if for nourishment or direction, assurance or inspiration. It is for these reasons that I re-read "The Stonemason," a play by Cormack McCarthy, who is best known for his novels, such as *All the Pretty Horses* and *Suttree*.

The play is set in Louisville Kentucky in the 1970's and is narrated by Ben Telfair, a stonemason whose father, Big Ben, and his grandfather, Papaw, are also stonemasons (papaw is a common name for a grandfather in the South.) It is a masterfully written story of a family faced with the acute problem of Ben's wayward nephew, Soldier, who is in trouble with the law. The play has a number of important layers, but the soul of the work, and the reason I read it over and over, is Papaw, the 100-year-old stonemason. With spiritual wisdom about what really matters in life, his passion intimately weaves the sanctity of work and craftsmanship into a single fabric. He reminds me of the craftsmen who built medieval cathedrals with pride of craftsmanship and with an acute sense of the nobility and sanctity of their work.

Ben recognizes the knowledge and wisdom that Papaw offers and he avidly tries to soak it up before Papaw is gone. When he realizes what a remarkable and unique resource his grandfather is, he says, "Oh I could hardly believe my good fortune. I swore then I would cleave to that old man like a bride." Neither Big Ben nor Soldier places a high value on Papaw's views of stonemasonry and his exacting standards.

During the course of the play, Papaw relates through Ben's narration what he knows and how he feels about stonemasonry, and not coincidentally, about life. He is also speaking to us about how one loves and respects his work: the truth of it, the wholeness of it, the essence of it. For Papaw, how he approaches his work is inextricably linked to how he views the world, how he treats others, and how this is all intertwined with his basic faith.

Here are excerpts from the play. While Ben and Papaw are working on a farmhouse, Ben the narrator speaks about stonemasonry:

"For true masonry is not held together by cement but by gravity. By the stuff of creation itself. The keystone that locks the arch is pressed in place by the thumb of God. When the weather is good we gather the stone ourselves out of the fields. What he likes best is what I like: To take the stone out of the ground and dress it and put it in place. We split the stone out along their seams. The chisels clink. The black earth smells good. He [Papaw] talks about stone in a different way from my father [Big Ben]. Always as a thing of consequence. As if the mason were a custodian of sorts. He speaks of sap in the stone. And fire. Of course he's right. You can smell it in the broken rock. He always watched my eyes to see if I understood. Or if I cared. I cared very much. I do now. According to the gospel of the true mason God has laid the stones in the earth for men to use and he has laid them in their bedding planes to show the mason how his work must go. A wall is made the same way the world is made."

There are physicians who have the same respect, almost reverence, for their patients. Perhaps for them it is because the mystery of their lives is held together "by the stuff of creation itself" and deserves—no, demands—professional and personal respect.

Ben continues, describing the essence of the work. "So. It's not the mortar that holds the work together. What holds the stone trues the wall as well and I've seen him check his fourfoot wooden level with a plumb bob and then break the level over the wall and call for a new one. Not in anger, but only to safeguard the true. To safeguard it everywhere...I see him standing there over his plumb bob which never lies and never lies and the plumb bob is pointing motionless to the unimaginable center of the earth four thousand miles beneath his feet. Pointing to a blackness unknown and unknowable both in truth and in principle where God and matter are locked in a collaboration that is silent nowhere in the universe and it is this that guides him as he places one stone over two and two over one as did his fathers before him and his sons to follow and let the rain carve them if it can."

Ben then talks about seeing samples of Papaw's work, some of it 80 years old, while driving in the region. "...in a thousand structures I've never seen a misplaced stone...The beauty of those structures would appear to be just a sort of a by-product, something fortuitous, but of course it is not. The aim of the mason was to make the wall stand up and that was his purpose in its entirety. The beauty of the stonework is simply a reflection of the purity of the mason's intention."

Papaw and Ben feel a passionate responsibility to their profession and for its integrity. They believe what they do matters not only for the quality of the wall they build, which can be seen by all, but also for what cannot be seen, what almost no one will know or understand or value. They do things right out of respect for their profession, their craft and most of all, out of respect for themselves. The characters that disdain such values, Big Ben and Soldier, are chronically unhappy and unfulfilled and find it hard to love unconditionally. They make excuses for their unhappiness, their impatience and the short cuts taken in their work and in their lives. For them, too, their jaded and cynical views of work are of one piece with their views of life.

The message is clear: Integrity in one's work and a passion for doing the right thing and doing things right are an inseparable part of what we love and value, of what brings happiness. Medicine is the same. Doing the work that we love is a privilege and a blessing; doing it with the same integrity and passion for truth as Papaw is the way we respect our patients, our profession, and ourselves.

Art and Craftsmanship in Medical Practice

Even before I went to medical school I had heard that the practice of medicine is both art and science, but I didn't know exactly what that meant. The science part was easy—it was all around us in pre-med and medical school. But how was it an art?

Art is defined as a creative process that starts with an idea and makes something unique, such as a painting or a rendition of an operatic aria. But the practice of medicine is largely a problem-solving process. Only the fourth definition of "art" in my dictionary even touches on medicine, "a skill at doing a specified thing, typically one acquired through practice;" pretty thin gruel. Another use of the term is exemplified by the "Art of Oncology" series in the *Journal of Clinical Oncology*, which deals with practical, psychological and emotional issues of both patient and doctor.

However, recent information from an unlikely source provides another facet of what is meant. *Shop Class and Soulcraft: An Inquiry into the Value of Work*, by Matthew B. Crawford, is an intriguing combination of philosophy, which the author has studied at length, psychology, and his personal experience as an electrician and a motorcycle mechanic, which he still is. The book begins by lamenting the disappearance of shop classes in high schools and the misguided ideal of preparing every student for college. His basic points are that with some guidance and training some students are capable of becoming master craftsmen resulting in satisfying and rewarding professional lives. He believes that some students are not suited for college, irrespective of their intellectual horsepower:

"The trades are then a natural home for anyone who would live by his own powers, free not only of deadening abstraction but also of the insidious hopes and rising insecurities that seem to be endemic in our current economic life."

He then proceeds to describe, with considerable eloquence

and conviction, the joys and satisfaction of becoming a crafts-man - a master mechanic, for example - and of working with one's hands. He contrasts this to the jobs of most people in modern society. They are distant from the final product, a cog in a large wheel, and feel little personal satisfaction or respon-sibility when the result is a car rolling off an assembly line in another state or country. The master craftsman's work, with its successes and failures, is clearly his own for all to see, whether he works alone or with a crew, as in building a house, with each trade responsible for a specific, self-contained aspect of the job.

"There is pride of accomplishment in the performance of whole tasks that can be held in the mind all at once, and con-templated as a whole once finished." The electrician knows he has succeeded if the lights go on. "In most work that tran-spires in large organizations, one's work is meaningless taken by itself. The individual feels that, alone, he is without any effect... This predisposes him to be deferential to the authority exercised in the organization...since the organization is that which gives meaning to his work."

Crawford then moves to what is, for me at least, the heart of the book. This includes a lengthy quote that I cannot adequately summarize. It begins when he speaks of his realization of the nature of being a mechanic:

"What I have learned is that mechanical work has a chancy, elusive character... even for expert mechanics. Aristotle can help here. He expanded the idea of art, or techne, to include those cases where our efforts are less than fully effective. In doing so, he steers a course between impotent fatalism and its opposite, a fantasy of complete mastery. Some arts reliably attain their object [like building a building or painting a picture]. But there is another class of arts that Aristotle calls 'stochastic' ['randomly determined,' from the Greek for 'aim at, guess'].

"An example is medicine. Mastery of a stochastic art is compatible with failure to achieve its end (health). As Aristotle writes, 'It does not belong to medicine to produce health, but only to promote it as much as possible...' Fixing things, whether cars or human bodies, is very different from building things from scratch. The mechanic and the doctor deal with failure every day, even if they are expert, whereas the builder does not. This is because the things that they [mechanics and doctors] fix are not of their own making [author's italics], and are therefore never known in a comprehensive or absolute way. The experience of failure tempers the conceit of mastery."

He goes on to say that any discipline that deals with an authoritative independent reality, such as a patient or a broken motorcycle, requires honesty and humility. "I believe this is especially so for the stochastic arts that fix things, such as doctoring and wrenching, in which we are not the makers of the things we tend... If we fail to respond appropriately to these authoritative realities, we remain idiots. If we succeed, we experience the pleasure that comes with progressively more acute vision, and the growing sense that our actions are fitting or just, as we bring them into conformity with that vision."

It goes without saying that a sick patient is not a broken motorcycle. But in both cases the work of fixing a problem operates with the tools of science and art at a very high level. Both artists physically touch and probe and try to visualize the problem as part of the whole entity, the patient or the complex machine, on the way to devising a solution. Both regularly succeed, or fail and try again.

This description of the art of medicine makes sense to me as a physician of 50 years, perhaps because I have been a physician for 50 years. It rings true partly because it avoids clichés and addresses the complexity head-on. The explanation is deeply and broadly considered in the larger context of life and being, of ethical and professional norms not limited to medicine, which can be excessively self-referential at times, as if our profession were completely unique. It also comes from practical, hard-won experience, lending it a substantial degree of authenticity... with a boost from Aristotle who first defined the art of medicine.

Crawford has done what all authors wish to do: help the reader see with new eyes. He also provides this reader with a platform for further exploration of the intricacies of work in medicine. For example, Crawford helps explain why most doctors are staunch individualists.

The art of medicine might better be described then as an amalgam of science and craftsmanship; the foundation of science applied with the experience, judgment, humility, and ethical values of a master craftsman.

The Effect of Chance and Timing on Medical Careers

This past year included another household move for us, the impact of which I described in a recent column. It was our ninth move since I finished my training. It occurred to me that each environment had had a major influence on my career (duh!).

But in further recalling each job and location, the collective influence of chance and timing on the trajectory of my career gave me a jolt, so I dug deeper.

Each location has differed, of course, in geography, institutional and community culture, values and mores, personal relationships and personalities. And they also differed in a difficult to define characteristic that I shall call essence or soul, a feature that uniquely identifies that environment at that particular time. I believe that many physicians and professionals of all types have similar experiences. Examples from my own career follow.

My first job after training was at St. Jude Children's Research Hospital. My colleague at the University of Illinois, Dr. Charley Abildgaard, had visited there and was asked to consider a position, but he became determined to return to his home state of California. He told me that St. Jude was an interesting new place and suggested I look at the job. I had never heard of St. Jude. My wife and I had three small children and had lived our whole lives in Chicago. I had no job-hunting experience and no one gave me any advice on what to say or ask for. I was naïve to say the least. But I went to Memphis and met Donald Pinkel, the director, and half a dozen other faculty members. It was Christmas time so I joined a party at Pinkel's house (St. Jude was small enough to gather all faculty and some staff in his house).

By the end of the second day I was enthralled. Pinkel's vision, the compact size and youth of the institution (less than 5 years old at that moment) and the opportunity to test myself as an independent investigator were more than I had hoped for. At my exit interview Pinkel said, "I can offer a salary between seventeen and eighteen thousand. Well what do you think?" I said, "I'll take the job." He said, "No, you can't do that, you need to talk to your wife." Talk about naïve!

I called my wife and told her how excited I was and that we would discuss it when I got home. I told my boss, Dr. Irv Schulman, chair of pediatrics and a distinguished hematologist (co-discoverer of coagulation Factor IX), that I was considering a job in Memphis. He had made me an offer to join the faculty and stay in his lab. Schulman said something like, "Are you nuts? There is nothing down there in Memphis, no one to work with. St. Jude is new and may not survive; you are doing well here," etc. etc. Needless to say, we moved to Memphis, the best professional move I could have made, especially considering how inexperienced I was.

So if Charley hadn't visited St. Jude and concluded that he really wanted to return to California, I would never have gone to Memphis, I would have had a traditional academic career in Chicago and never would have had the opportunity to lead a large leukemia program and its clinical research. My focus in Chicago would have been non-malignant hematology. I would not have become director of St. Jude or physician-in-chief of Memorial Sloan-Kettering. I would not have become so active in ASCO and have started its Quality Oncology Practice Initiative. In other words, my career would have been dramatically different.

Among several other fateful incidents, another stands out for me. In the early 1990s Dr. John Mendelsohn, former president of MD Anderson, and I were in Madison, Wisconsin for a meeting of external advisors of Dr. Paul Carbone's University of Wisconsin Cancer Center. We shared a cab going to the airport when, out of the blue, John asked if I would consider being a candidate for the physician-in-chief job at Memorial Sloan-Kettering. John was the chair of medicine there at that time and I had heard that Dr. Vince De Vita had stepped down from that position after a relatively short tenure because of some differences of opinion. I said I wasn't sure.

About a month later I received a call from Dr. Paul Marks, president of MSK, asking me the same question. I said I would be willing to look. I had been at St. Jude for 24 years and the director for 9 years. I was happy and reasonably successful at St. Jude. But my plans for growth, development and reshaping the faculty were nearly complete. Also, I had come to believe that 10 years, plus or minus a couple, were about as long as a leader should head a creative organization like a medical school, academic department, or institute. In my experience most leaders who stayed longer became stagnant, overly conservative, dictatorial, or had expended their political capital. There were exceptions, but very few.

I visited MSK and found it to be an attractive opportunity professionally and personally. After a subsequent visit with my wife, I called friends and colleagues and former physicians-in-chiefs for their advice; the universal response was, "Don't do it!!" I heard a variety of reasons: Paul Marks is difficult to work with; some of the chairs are (fill in the blank); it is a large complex organization that is difficult to change; living in New York is a challenge.

I had a gut feeling it was the right job at the right time in my career and my wife agreed. I took the job and we moved to The City in an apartment that was walking distance to MSK. Marks was a gruff bully who didn't scare me one bit, so we actually got along pretty well. The chairs were largely cooperative and helpful. The medical staff was first rate up and down the line. The administrative and nursing staffs were outstanding. It was a privilege to be head of the medical staff and the hospital. My wife and I thoroughly enjoyed New York. Our kids were grown and gone so most of the time the rich culture made it like living in an adult Disneyland.

So a chance cab ride with John Mendelsohn and the specific timing in my tenure at St. Jude made it possible to take on a great job and learn a lot about adult oncology and the greater cancer world, which has served me well later.

So what did these (and other) experiences teach me that I would be willing to pass on?

1. You may plan all you want, but chance and timing will play a role in professional development much more than you tend to believe.

2. Listen to advice from friends and colleagues, but listen even more to your own gut feeling. (The one job I took that nearly every trusted advisor strongly recommended turned out to be a failure.)

3. At all times, know where you are on your professional growth curve; is your growth slowing or coming to an end?

4. Know whether you are you a risk-taker. I learned early in my professional life that I am a risk-taker; I enjoy new, and sometimes risky, challenges and I believe that most good opportunities knock only once. If you are risk-averse, then you may be much more cautious and prefer the comfort of the tried and true, even if your professional growth has slowed.

Socrates said it best; his guiding rule in life's journey is, "Know thyself." He might have added, "Be open-minded," or "Understand that chance and timing ("Fate") will influence your direction."

The Decline of Dignity and Civility

Now and then I read a column I wish I had written myself because of its excellence and because I had been thinking of the general topic but couldn't find the right handle to pull it together. David Brooks wrote such a column titled, "In Search of Dignity," for the 7 July 2009 issue of the *New York Times*.

In his column Brooks starts by recalling George Washington's practice, beginning at a young age, of trying diligently to follow over 100 "Rules of Civility and Decent Behavior in Company and Conversation." These rules came from a 16th-century guidebook and included: "Read no letter, books or paper in company" and "If any one come to speak to you while you are sitting, stand up." However, these were not only rules of etiquette, but were "designed to improve inner morals by shaping the outward man."

Brooks points out that Washington became "a new kind of hero;" he wasn't so much a political or military hero, but as historian Gordon Wood has written, "Washington became a great man and was acclaimed as a classical hero because of the way he conducted himself during times of temptation. It was his moral character that set him off from other men."

Washington came to personify what Brooks calls, the "dignity code," based on the premise "that human beings are flawed creatures who live in constant peril of falling into disasters caused by their own passions." So systems were necessary to balance and restrain those desires. (This sounds a bit like the Catholic catechism of my youth, but Washington's focus was secular behavior, particularly in public service.) "The dignity code commanded its followers to be disinterested—to endeavor to put national interests above personal interests. It commanded followers to be reticent—to never degrade intimate emotions by parading them in public. It also commanded its followers to be dispassionate—to distrust rashness, zealotry, fury and enthusiasm."

Brooks then points out that this dignity code was largely in effect for some time. For most of American history, politicians did not even publicly campaign for president, which was thought to be "ruinously corrupting." (Oh, where have you gone, George Washington, now that we need you even more?)

Even though Americans have continued to admire people who seem naturally dignified (e.g. Joe DiMaggio, Tom Hanks, Ronald Reagan, Martin Luther King, Jr.), the code of dignity "has been obliterated," according to Brooks. He blames capitalism and its culture of self-promotion, the "cult of naturalism" which tells us to liberate our feelings, charismatic evangelism which encourages public confession, and "radical egalitarianism and its hostility to aristocratic manners." In other words, the bulldozer of modern life has buried the dignity code.

He is dismayed by the scandals, seemingly weekly, featuring people who simply do not know how to act: Governor Mark Sanford's lack of any sense of reticence in his rambling self-exposure in the face of disgrace.

Then came the public's sanctification of Michael Jackson, who in life was "apparently untouched by any pressure to live according to the rules and restraints of adulthood." And Sarah Palin's now famous press conference. In the latter case, Brooks describes her as "a woman who aspires to a high public role but is unfamiliar with the traits of equipoise and constancy, which are the sources of authority and trust. In each of these events, one sees people who simply have no social norms to guide them as they try to navigate the currents of their own passions."

Some readers may consider Brooks an old fuddy-duddy who is living in the past. But I count myself in Brooks's camp on this matter; the past has a great deal to teach us about living in and contributing to a civil society. As a whole, too many of us have lost our bearings when it comes to simple manners and behavior that is guided by civility, dignity and humility. In any life, this may be due to a lack of exemplars. Today, even when I ask women to precede me at a door or when I pull the chair out at table for them (old habits die hard), they are often surprised and, sadly, a little embarrassed. The original meaning of "gentleman," according to my 6th grade teacher, was "a gentle man, one who is well-mannered and considerate of others." In my dictionary, it is sad to say, that definition is now second behind, "a man of gentle or noble birth."

I believe technology has catalyzed this process. Reality and "talk show" TV where thoughtful decorum and humility are the antithesis of a "successful" program that is defined, basically, as an exposition of one's private affairs, weaknesses and vulnerabilities. The relentless and voracious 24/7/365 appetite of the multitude of competing news and entertainment shows further encourages a culture of "peeping tomism" and schadenfreude (taking pleasure in another's misfortune). Facebook and Twitter are another expression of this seeming compulsion to share one's private life with anyone and everyone. On this issue, if there were a "Civility and Dignity Curmudgeon Club," I would join eagerly.

Closer to home, our professional behavior too often reflects a lack of civility, dignity, and grace, which can color and degrade our professional and personal social interactions. The failure to knock at a patient's hospital room door before entering or to address the patient respectfully by their family name or to ask if there is anything one may do for the patient before departing, all indicate a lack of appropriate respect. More serious and dismaying, deliberately misleading patients, shouting at nurses, and throwing instruments have not disappeared. Disregarding the small civil and dignified behaviors, George Washington would contend, influences behavior in the big things.

The habit of civility contributes to our moral fiber, which in most of us is frayed and needs all the repeated shoring up we can muster. Thank goodness, being a gentle man or gentle woman persists even today as a desirable and laudatory trait. Though modern times may not be conducive to such behavior, we all still recognize it and respect it when we see it, especially when we are the beneficiaries. We try to teach our kids to be polite and considerate of others...we also should examine our own daily behavior and make course corrections now and then.

Physicians at Their Peak

I don't know much about Olympic swimmers or professional quarterbacks, but by my unscientific observation, I would guess that a top notch swimmer probably peaks in competitive ability at about 20 years of age, give or take 4 years or so. I would also guess that competitive professional quarterback probably peaks at about 30 years of age, give or take 4 years or so. By that I mean that they will not consistently perform substantially better after reaching that peak. Subsequently, they will perform at about the same level for a while and some time later, slowly or rapidly, progressively get worse. They may still perform satisfactorily, but not at their historically best level. There are exceptions, but the variations are most likely to be when the decline occurs, not if it will occur. A decline is inevitable.

I have often wondered when physicians reach their peak of skill as a doctor. To be clear, I am speaking of physicians as practicing doctors who provide ongoing care for patients on a consistent basis. Of course, this is not easy to measure (maybe impossible) so my attempts to tease this out cannot be a straight line because we have no quantitative comparatives, such as swimmers' race times and gold medals or quarterbacks' touchdowns and interceptions, to use as a gauge.

This is basically a personal reflection of my six-decade span as a physician and as one who has observed, trained, worked with and judged many physicians. My focus is on physicians as practitioners of the art and science of medicine face-to-face with patients, not as a chair of medicine, leader of a practice group, laboratory scientist or any other related professional activities that physicians may enter.

The first challenge in this exercise is what is meant by peak? Peak of what? Surgical or other technical skills, diagnostic skills, compassion, knowledge? Wrestling with these questions led to my approaching the issue from a slanted angle rather than head on.

When I view the evolution of physicians' abilities, I believe there are at least three overlapping phases. The first is experience. This is the basis for all the rest. The next is intellectual insight, which combines experience and knowledge acquired from experience and indirectly from publications, meetings, grand rounds, colleagues and students. The third stage is humility, knowing the boundaries of one's ability and the common sense to act accordingly. Humility implies that one is open to becoming wise, to acquiring wisdom. This is the opposite of the know-it-all.

Each of these three qualities can be, and usually are, expanded over time and each reaches a peak, often independent of the other two. For example, an experienced and knowledgeable surgeon with long experience and excellent technical skills may remain infantile when it comes to humility and tends to inflate the accolades he receives to justify acting beyond his experience, knowledge, and skills. I can think of examples for radiation and medical oncologists as well.

If a physician lacks one of the three pillars described above-- experience, intellectual curiosity with knowledge, and humility—it would be impossible to reach a high level of medical practice. The peak of one's ability would not be "competitive" and it would be difficult to imagine such a practice being even satisfactory. The degree to which one raises his/her skill level in all three of these qualities will collectively determine the peak of skillful medical practice.

For this purpose, one may encompass all these qualities into a single "measure" (really an attribute) of peak ability and skill: wisdom. Experience, intellectual curiosity, knowledge, sensitivity to patients and their needs, and a measured balance of good judgment and humility contribute to what we might call, "medical wisdom," which includes the application of all three qualities.

Let's digress for a bit about "wisdom." First, here is a short poem:

The Road to Wisdom by Piet Hein (Danish poet)

> The road to wisdom? Well, it's plain
> And simple to express:
> Err
> and err
> and err again,
> but less
> and less
> and less.

This reinforces the idea that wisdom comes from experience, learning and the ability to accept that one has erred (or observed another who erred) and change one's practice, the latter being a sign of medical wisdom.

So back to the initial question: When do physicians reach their peak? It may vary a bit by specialty, but my guess is that most physicians are at their best and have reached their balanced peak in their forties or mid fifties. They may reach their peak of technical skill, knowledge base, or intellectual curiosity earlier, but wisdom is like a fine red wine, it takes longer to develop. I have known physicians who remained at or near that peak in all three qualities well into their sixties, but more often there is a decline in stamina or enthusiasm, or distraction with other duties that causes slippage; slippage in one area may be mitigated if the pillar of wisdom stays strong and a humble mind stays open.

Of course, some of this speculation is autobiographical. In my own case, I thought I was the best pediatric hematologist-oncologist on earth in my thirties, a clear lack of humility. I believe I reached my peak as a physician in my early forties and remained close to that level until about a decade later. I accrued administrative responsibility by then and eventually started to lose track of antibiotic doses and much of my imaging skill due to a lack of use. The fellows and nurse practitioners knew more about many details than I did.

When I left St. Jude for Memorial Sloan-Kettering in my mid fifties, I realized that I could not and should not assume primary responsibility for patients because of this decline and because I was undertaking a full time administrative job and would not be readily available to patients and families. Interestingly, I found I could still think about and discuss clinical problems clearly (as in rounds and conferences) and retained what I believe was good judgment for quite a while; technical day-to-day bedside knowledge declined first and analytic wisdom faded last.

It is humbling to realize that, in my view, despite all my training and experience and study, I was at my very best as a physician for only 10-15 years. I like to think I was pretty good before and after that period, but who can say? Certainly not

Humility is the only one of the three pillars that I believe has continued to grow in my case, and justifiably so. A review like this is one reason why.

Smiley and Me

I shall officially retire for the second time in a few weeks. Friends laugh when I tell them this news and make one of the following comments: "I thought you retired a long time ago," or "Ha ha, you will never retire," or "What do you have lined up next?" The latter group knows me well enough to understand my definition of retirement: the ability to work at what I like to do for only as long as I want, to accept only work that is interesting to me, and to have the freedom to work a little or a lot.

In our discussions before my first retirement, my wife Pat reminded me that retirement was not a long weekend; it was a career change. Some can happily retire to golfing, fishing or favorite hobbies; that is not for me. I wanted something that was intellectually stimulating and in the field that I know best – cancer medicine. That led to my establishing a one-man consulting business serving cancer centers and cancer programs; helping them improve their organizations, increase efficiency and compete successfully for grants has been my main focus for over a decade.

But I have come to realize that there is a deeper reason for staying active. I no longer do cancer research or provide personal care to cancer patients but I am still deeply engaged, intellectually and emotionally, in the cancer problem. Trying to understand and manage cancer is a lifelong pursuit that I cannot let go completely.

Which brings me to Smiley. George Smiley is a character in two spy novels written by John le Carré. The first, *Tinker, Tailor, Soldier, Spy*, was made into a movie in 1979 and the sequel, *Smiley's People*, was made into a TV series released by the BBC in 1982. Both were highly celebrated productions. The central character, George Smiley, played by Alec Guinness in both productions, was a senior member of the British spy agency (the "Circus") who, in "Tinker" was given the task of finding a high level Soviet spy within the British agency. It goes without saying that he found him.

In *Smiley's People* he is called out of retirement to settle the affairs of a friend, a Russian living in the West who had done some work for the Circus. His friend had been murdered. Smiley finds his old organization so overwhelmed by political considerations that it doesn't want to know what happened. He begins to follow up the clues of his friend's last days, discovering that they lead to a high person in the Russian secret service and to a secret important enough for that person to kill for. Smiley continues to put together the pieces using all his contacts and good will with various agents in the Circus and elsewhere in Britain and Europe to try to find the secret that the high level Russian agent fears so much.

Near the end of episode four of the six on DVD, he is sitting in a car driven by a young member of the Circus who questions him. Why is he pushing ahead with the investigation when the leaders asked him to stop? Why has he become a rogue agent setting up shop independent of the leaders? Why doesn't he just stay retired and take care of his wife?" His answer follows.

"In my time I have seen Whitehall skirts go up and come down again, heard all the excuses for doing nothing and reaped the consequent frightful harvest. I've watched people hop up and down and call it progress. I have seen good men go to the wall while the idiots get promoted with dazzling regularity. All I'm left with is me plus 30-odd years of Cold War without the options. ("So what does that mean?" says the young agent.) It means that if a rogue elephant comes at me out of the thicket in my path and I get a shot at it I intend to shoot it dead with a minimum of force."

This struck a chord in me and provoked some thoughts about the similarities of the "Circus" to the world we live and work in. The phrase, "skirts go up and come down again," reminds me that we are too often uncritical slaves to fashion, to the latest "cure" or new combination therapy without objective evidence of value; autologous marrow transplants for breast cancer and proton beam therapy are two examples. "...heard all the excuses for doing nothing," matches the comfortable, recalcitrant bureaucracies in our institutions, local and national, that often attack problems by forming another committee or focus group or summit that are as futile as the last ones. "...hop up and down and call it progress," perfectly describes many cancer clinical trials. "...good men go to the wall while the idiots get promoted with dazzling regularity," speaks for itself.

But like Smiley, one reason I and other "old cancer guys" (OCGs) continue our activities in the cancer world is the opportunity to take another shot at the "rogue elephant" we have been fighting throughout our careers. Like Smiley, our guns may not have the power that they once had so we are left with "minimum force," but any way we can help people deal with cancer better is worth the effort. Irrespective of the outcome of the efforts of Smiley and us OCGs, we want to give it a try and get off as many shots as we can while we can.